no sweeter than the

RIPEST CHERRY

A Seven-Day Culinary Guide for Radiant Health

by **SUZIE BOHANNON**

No Sweeter Than The Ripest Cherry ISBN 978-0-9887680-0-0 Published by Honest Abe Press. Cover copyright © 2013 Suzie Bohannon. All Rights Reserved. "Super Nutrition Appendix" copyright © 2013 Suzie Bohannon. All Rights Reserved. Barring journalistic intent, no part of this publication may be reproduced or transmitted without prior written permission from the publisher. Concept by Waska Lamb and Suzie Bohannon. Written by Suzie Bohannon. Photography by Javiera Estrada. Line Art and Coloring by Suzie Bohannon. Modeling by Etana Jacobsen and James Stinson. Recipes by Suzie Bohannon. Food Styling by Suzie Bohannon and Waska Lamb. Edited by Tai Carmen. Cover Art by Suzie Bohannon. Publication design by Suzie Bohannon and Waska Lamb. Source image "Oak Tree" on cover by Tena Valenti. Source image "Avocado!" on page 21 by Flickr/walknboston. All characters, their distinctive likeness and related elements featured in this publication are trademarks of Suzie Bohannon and Honest Abe Press, Inc. The stories, characters, and incidents featured in this publication are entirely fictional. The information contained in this book is based on research and personal experience. This book is not intended to diagnose, treat, prevent, or cure any illness or disease. Honest Abe Press, Inc. P.O. Box 618, Topanga, CA 90290. Published in the U.S.A. First Printing, Issue One. www.ripestcherry.com

what you hold in your hands is the gift of a dear friend...

When I was growing up, my mother did her best to steer
me clear of sugar, caffeine and processed foods. But like
most kids, I fought her nutritional advice every step of
the way, threatening starvation and demanding sugared cereals
and white bread!★ At some point though, her message seeped in and
a lifelong love of food and nutrition emerged. For the last sixteen
years I have been a raw food enthusiast and worked as a raw food
chef, creating menus and teaching recipe classes -- both privately
and at various retreat centers and restaurants across the USA. Up
until this point, I have been giving little handwritten prescriptions
for health and wellbeing to loved ones seeking nutritional advice. I
am so excited to finally be able to offer my recipes and health tips to
you in such a thrilling format! The teachings presented herein have been
garnered through personal experimentation, intuition, research and pure
divination. Let this knowledge be an homage to the practice of spontaneous
information sharing. This guide is not meant to treat, prevent, diagnose,
or cure any disease, but hopefully it will provoke an examination of the
way you nourish your body. May it inspire you in simple and convenient
ways to positively transform your heath -- and help you start
connecting the dots between what you eat and how you feel.
Use this guide simply to experience new recipes, or as a week long
template for integrating more living food into your diet. This comic
book is not meant to be dogmatic or precious in any way. Abuse it!
Splatter it with soy sauce and flaxseed oil. Fold it up in your
back pocket for a trip to the grocery store. Write notes in
it. Reinvent the recipes, mix up the salad dressings, eat
the same thing every day -- make this comic book
your field guide to feeling great for a season!

Love,

COMIC BOOK INGREDIENTS:
(otherwise known as a table of contents)

★And please know that every once in a while, I still eat a bag of cheese puffs.

Another beautiful day breaks...

...but not so for Ingrid, stuck in a pre-coffee funk.

HATE MORNING.

GO AWAY!

NEED COFFEE...

Unrested, undernourished, and fed up with feeling run down, Ingrid pleads to the universe for ideas.

SOMEBODY, ANYBODY, HELP ME FEEL YOUNG AGAIN... I'M SO TIRED!

MAYBE I SHOULD CALL IN SICK?

WHAT'S THIS? DO I HEAR THE SOUNDS OF A STRUGGLE WITH MY OLD FOE "SELF-SABOTAGE?" THIS SOUNDS LIKE A JOB FOR THE "SUPER SUBCONSCIOUS!"

PERHAPS BREAKFAST WILL HELP. LET'S SEE... WHAT HAVE I GOT?

INGRID? CAN YOU HEAR ME? YOU DESERVE BETTER THAN WHATEVER YOU'VE GOT IN THAT MOLD HOTEL YOU CALL A FRIDGE!

OH JOY.

OLD CHINESE FOOD.

UH OH. I MUST ACT QUICKLY...!

WHAT'S THIS...?

A RECIPE BOOK?

DOESN'T LOOK LIKE A RECIPE BOOK.

LOOK'S MORE LIKE SOME... WEIRD... COMIC BOOK!

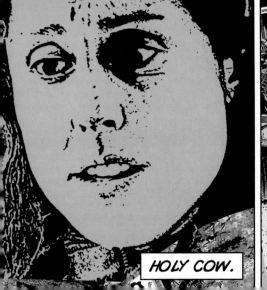

HOLY COW.

THIS CAN'T BE HAPPENING... THIS IS ME!

AND THAT'S ME SAYING "THIS IS ME!"

Understandably, Ingrid found herself feeling rather disturbed by her present circumstances.

Even though the book lay several feet away on the floor, Ingrid felt like she was still holding it in her hands...

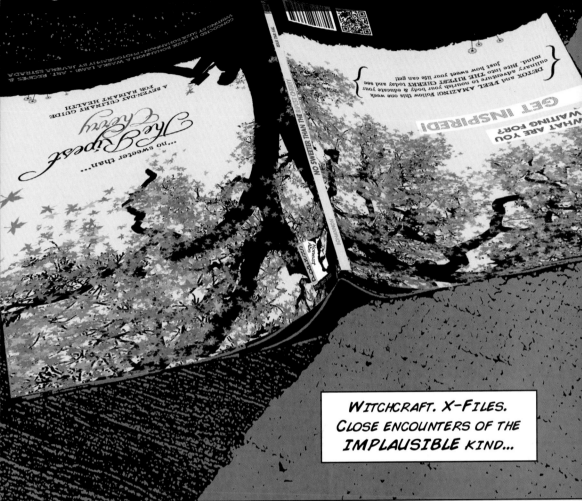

WITCHCRAFT. X-FILES. CLOSE ENCOUNTERS OF THE *IMPLAUSIBLE* KIND...

...AND YET...

WHY AM I *STRANGELY COMPELLED* TO DISCOVER WHAT I DO NEXT?

THE TIME HAS COME TO TAKE CARE OF YOURSELF!

THROW OUT ALL THE CRAP IN YOUR FRIDGE...

...AND GET YOUR BUNS DOWN TO THE NEAREST HEALTH FOOD STORE.

GOSH, THESE STORES ARE *EVERYWHERE!*

GUESS I SHOULD GET WHATEVER I DON'T ALREADY HAVE ON THESE LISTS, HUH?

YES!! THE LISTS ON THE NEXT FEW PAGES DETAIL EXACTLY WHAT YOU WILL NEED TO MAKE EVERY SINGLE RECIPE IN THIS BOOK FOR THE NEXT WEEK! THE AMOUNTS LISTED WILL FEED ONE PERSON, WITH SOME LEFTOVERS.

SAVE YOURSELF SOME $$$ AND DOUBLE CHECK YOUR PANTRY BEFORE YOU GO TO THE STORE. YOU PROBABLY ALREADY HAVE SOME OF THESE INGREDIENTS!

DRIED HERBS & SPICES
(in alphabetical order)

Black Pepper
Cayenne
Chipotle powder (grind in a coffee grinder!)
Cinnamon
Clove
Cumin
Curry
Dill
Garam Masala
Onion flakes
Paprika
Pink Himalayan & Smoked Sea Salt
Turmeric

LIQUID SEASONINGS:
(in no particular order)

Raw Coconut Nectar
Raw Honey
Raw Apple Cider Vinegar (optional)
Almond Extract
Balsamic Vinegar
Ume Plum Vinegar
Stone Crushed Olive Oil
Toasted Sesame Oil
Cold Pressed Coconut Oil
Black Truffle Oil (optional)
Bragg's Liquid Aminos
Ground Vanilla Bean or Extract
Nama Shoyu

THE TRUFFLE OIL IS AN OPTIONAL INGREDIENT, SO IF IT'S TOO COSTLY OR TIME CONSUMING TO TRACK DOWN, DON'T WORRY ABOUT IT... BUT BOY DOES IT MAKE THINGS YUMMY!

PRODUCE THE PRODUCE!
(listed somewhat by type)

7 avocados

1 bunch each chard, collard & kale

1 bunch romaine

1 bunch watercress

1 large tub mixed greens

1 box of sprouts

1 bag of sunflower sprouts (optional)

8 Persian cucumbers

1 summer squash

1 bunch of celery

1 ear of corn

4 small tomatoes

10 green beans

2 okras

1 burdock root

1 bunch radishes

1 medium Jerusalem artichoke

3 large carrots

1 medium golden beet

1 yam (NOT sweet potato!)

2 red potatoes

1 very large bunch of ginger

1 portabella mushroom

1/2 c. shitake or oyster mushrooms

2 T. maitake mushrooms (optional)

WHEN IT COMES TO PRODUCE, IT'S GOOD TO BE CHOOSY. PAY ATTENTION TO SYMMETRY, COLOR, TURGIDITY AND OVERALL FRESHNESS. AS A RULE, AVOID PRODUCE THAT LOOKS BATTERED AND WILTED, OR FEELS MUSHY. CRISP APPLES FEEL LIKE ROCKS. RIPE PAPAYAS FEEL LIKE SOFT CLAY. RIPE AVOCADOS, LIKE A COOL STICK OF BUTTER.

FRUITS AND SWEET THINGS...
(organized by sweetness)

2 limes

11 lemons

1 package cranberries

1 package frozen raspberries

1 package fresh raspberries (optional)

1 package frozen blueberries

1 package fresh strawberries

2 apples (you may want extras)

1 qt. apple juice, unpasteurized

1 pear

2 bananas

2 young coconuts

HERBS, ALLIUMS & PEPPERS
(listed by kind)

1 bunch basil

1 bunch Italian parsley

1 bunch cilantro

sage (dry or fresh)

rosemary (dry or fresh)

thyme (dry or fresh)

fresh mint (optional)

4 medium shallots

2 garlic bulbs

1 red onion

1 bunch green onions

1 jalapeno pepper

GOLLY, MY WHOLE BASKET IS FILLING UP WITH VEGETABLES!

THAT'S RIGHT! DON'T BE AFRAID (THEY WON'T BITE)

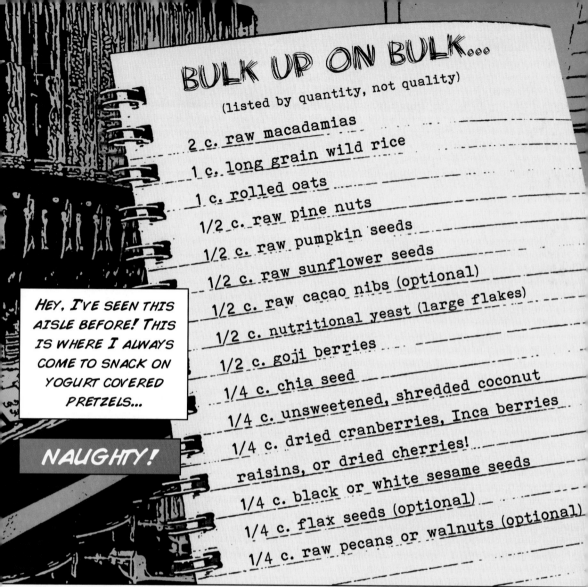

BULK UP ON BULK...

(listed by quantity, not quality)

- 2 c. raw macadamias
- 1 c. long grain wild rice
- 1 c. rolled oats
- 1/2 c. raw pine nuts
- 1/2 c. raw pumpkin seeds
- 1/2 c. raw sunflower seeds
- 1/2 c. raw cacao nibs (optional)
- 1/2 c. nutritional yeast (large flakes)
- 1/2 c. goji berries
- 1/4 c. chia seed
- 1/4 c. unsweetened, shredded coconut
- 1/4 c. dried cranberries, Inca berries, raisins, or dried cherries!
- 1/4 c. black or white sesame seeds
- 1/4 c. flax seeds (optional)
- 1/4 c. raw pecans or walnuts (optional)

HEY, I'VE SEEN THIS AISLE BEFORE! THIS IS WHERE I ALWAYS COME TO SNACK ON YOGURT COVERED PRETZELS...

NAUGHTY!

YOU MAY NOT FIND EVERYTHING IN THE BULK SECTION, AND THE AMOUNTS ARE ONLY FOR THE RECIPES THAT FOLLOW, SO GET A LITTLE EXTRA FOR SNACKING, EXPERIMENTATION AND DINNER FRIENDS! WHEN SELECTING NUTS & SEEDS, BE SURE TO GET THEM RAW. RAW NUTS AND SEEDS ARE NUTRITIONALLY SUPERIOR TO THEIR ROASTED COUNTERPARTS BECAUSE THEY CAN BE SPROUTED. SPROUTING IS A SIMPLE PROCESS WHICH CAN BOOST A SPROUT'S NUTRITIONAL CONTENT AND BIO-AVAILABILITY -- IN SOME INSTANCES BY OVER 600%![1] JUST THINK, LOCKED WITHIN A SINGLE NUT LIES THE GENETIC POTENTIAL OF A FULL GROWN TREE, WHICH CAN PRODUCE HUNDREDS OF THOU-SANDS OF NUTS DURING ITS LIFETIME. THE GROWTH CYCLE OF ALL SEEDS/NUTS/GRAINS/LEGUMES IS LARGELY KEPT DORMANT BY A COATING OF ABSCISIC ACID (ABA), A PLANT HORMONE THAT INHIBITS ENZYMATIC ACTIVITY AND PREVENTS GERMINATION.[2] AS AN ENZYME INHIBITOR, ABA ENABLES AN INTACT SEED TO SURVIVE DEHYDRATION AS WELL AS YOUR BODY'S ENZYMATIC DIGES-TIVE PROCESS -- WHICH COULD SUGGEST WHY NUT/SEED ALLERGIES ARE SO PREVALENT. IN ORDER TO ACTIVATE THE HORMONES WHICH GOVERN GERMINATION, THE ABA COATING THE SEED MUST BE REDUCED.[3] SOAKING A SEED IN WATER FOR SEVERAL HOURS IS ONE WAY TO RINSE AWAY ITS "ENZYMATIC INHIBITIONS" AND INITIATE A SEED'S TRANSFORMATION INTO A SPROUT -- A BABY PLANT! THIS IS WHY SPROUTED NUTS/SEEDS/GRAINS/LEGUMES ARE MORE ALKALINE, WHILE THEIR COOKED COUNTERPARTS ARE ACID FORMING. ACCORDING TO GARY NULL, PH.D., "EATING ALKALINE FOODS BALANCES THE PH OF THE BLOOD, WHICH, IN TURN, INHIBITS THE PROLIFERATION OF CANCER CELLS. ALKALINE FOODS KEEP THE BLOOD PH IN ITS IDEAL RANGE OF BETWEEN 7.2 AND 7.4, WHICH IS IMPORTANT FOR THE PREVENTION AND TREATMENT OF CANCER. IDEALLY, THE DIET SHOULD CONSIST OF 80 PERCENT ALKALINE-FORMING FOODS, SUCH AS THOSE AVAILABLE FROM MANY RAW FRUITS AND VEGETABLES, AS WELL AS NUTS, SEEDS, GRAINS, AND LEGUMES."[4]

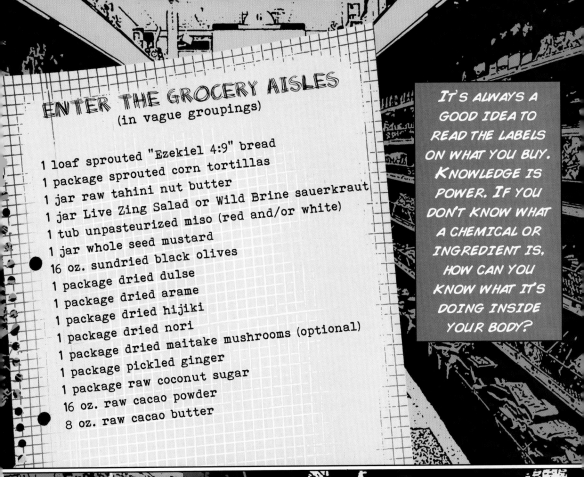

ENTER THE GROCERY AISLES
(in vague groupings)

1 loaf sprouted "Ezekiel 4:9" bread
1 package sprouted corn tortillas
1 jar raw tahini nut butter
1 jar Live Zing Salad or Wild Brine sauerkraut
1 tub unpasteurized miso (red and/or white)
1 jar whole seed mustard
16 oz. sundried black olives
1 package dried dulse
1 package dried arame
1 package dried hijiki
1 package dried nori
1 package dried maitake mushrooms (optional)
1 package pickled ginger
1 package raw coconut sugar
16 oz. raw cacao powder
8 oz. raw cacao butter

IT'S ALWAYS A GOOD IDEA TO READ THE LABELS ON WHAT YOU BUY. KNOWLEDGE IS POWER. IF YOU DON'T KNOW WHAT A CHEMICAL OR INGREDIENT IS, HOW CAN YOU KNOW WHAT IT'S DOING INSIDE YOUR BODY?

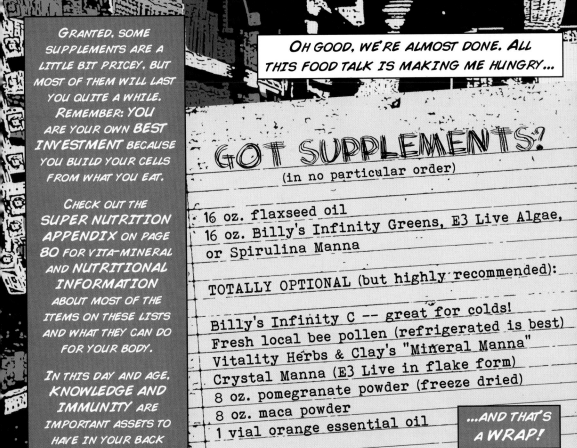

GRANTED, SOME SUPPLEMENTS ARE A LITTLE BIT PRICEY, BUT MOST OF THEM WILL LAST YOU QUITE A WHILE. REMEMBER: YOU ARE YOUR OWN BEST INVESTMENT BECAUSE YOU BUILD YOUR CELLS FROM WHAT YOU EAT.

CHECK OUT THE SUPER NUTRITION APPENDIX ON PAGE 80 FOR VITA-MINERAL AND NUTRITIONAL INFORMATION ABOUT MOST OF THE ITEMS ON THESE LISTS AND WHAT THEY CAN DO FOR YOUR BODY.

IN THIS DAY AND AGE, KNOWLEDGE AND IMMUNITY ARE IMPORTANT ASSETS TO HAVE IN YOUR BACK POCKET.

OH GOOD, WE'RE ALMOST DONE. ALL THIS FOOD TALK IS MAKING ME HUNGRY...

GOT SUPPLEMENTS?
(in no particular order)

16 oz. flaxseed oil
16 oz. Billy's Infinity Greens, E3 Live Algae, or Spirulina Manna

TOTALLY OPTIONAL (but highly recommended):

Billy's Infinity C -- great for colds!
Fresh local bee pollen (refrigerated is best)
Vitality Herbs & Clay's "Mineral Manna"
Crystal Manna (E3 Live in flake form)
8 oz. pomegranate powder (freeze dried)
8 oz. maca powder
1 vial orange essential oil

...AND THAT'S A WRAP!

WOWSERS! BOY AM I **EXCITED** TO GET HOME AND RESTOCK MY KITCHEN!

GOSH, WHAT A DIFFERENCE.

IT'S LIKE MY FRIDGE GOT A $250 FACIAL!

OKAY, NOW THAT YOUR FOOD SCENE IS MORE IN ORDER, LET'S MAKE SURE YOU'VE GOT THE PROPER TOOLS TO MAKE THE RECIPES. *A COFFEE GRINDER & CHAMPION JUICER* ARE VERY HELPFUL, BUT IF YOU HAVEN'T GOT THEM *DON'T WORRY!* ALL YOU REALLY NEED IS A *GOOD BLENDER,* SINCE MOST OF THE COMING RECIPES ARE SMOOTHIES, SAUCES & SALAD DRESSINGS.

PHEW, THAT'S A RELIEF! SO WHAT OTHER EQUIPMENT DO I NEED?

...FOOD PROCESSOR...?

THANK GOODNESS FOR THAT GARAGE SALE!

Wondermixer

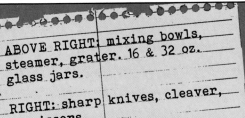

ABOVE RIGHT: mixing bowls, steamer, grater. 16 & 32 oz. glass jars.

RIGHT: sharp knives, cleaver, & scissors.

BELOW: rubber "child cheater" spatulas, mixing spoons, garlic press, spatula, peeler, zester, strainer, some tupperware, measuring cups & spoons, as well as...

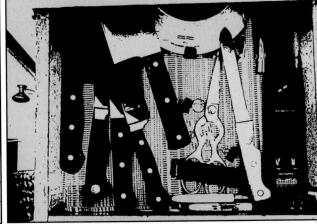

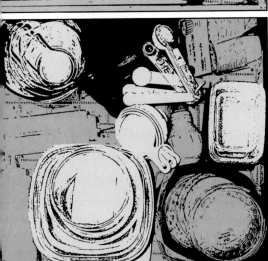

...A GOOD CUTTING BOARD?

CHECK! WHAT ELSE?

COURAGE *AND* *IMAGINATION.*

"Sunday morning, rain is falling..."

-- Maroon 5

The season to fall in LOVE

THE SEASONS FOR SNUGGLING have arrived at last. There's a bite in the morning air and a wisp of wood smoke on the breeze. Autumn has come again, and with the deepening reds on the trees comes the last flush of garden varietals designed to prime you for the cold months ahead.

In Chinese medicine, the Metal element associated with the fall affects the lungs, large intestine (nutrient assimilation & toxin elimination), and the skin.[5] During the fall these body systems are activated, working hard to prepare you for the winter months, and thus are more susceptible to deficiencies as nature shifts from yang to the beginning of the yin cycle. Activities you can engage in to support these organs include dry skin brushing, colon cleansing, taking extra probiotics/eating cultured foods, and getting as much fresh, clean air as possible.[6] Certain foods can also provide support; Steven Sonmore, L.Ac. suggests that during the fall "moderate amounts of pungent foods like garlic, onions, ginger, horseradish, and mustard are beneficial to the lungs."[7] On an emotional level, autumn months in Chinese Medicine are about grief and letting go.[8] Is there something you're holding onto that you're ready to release and let fall away like a dry leaf? Now is the time to harvest what you've gleaned from the summer, and come inside to get organized for winter months of inward activities & introspection.

The brilliant red, yellow, orange, and deep green colors of the autumn harvest hail the presence of CAROTENOIDS. These phytonutrient pigment compounds, like beta-carotene and lycopene, happen to be some of the best antioxidants in nature.[9] In case you're wondering, antioxidants are crucial because they neutralize the "free radicals" your cells produce as byproducts to substances like stress hormones and cigarette smoke. "In humans, the most common form of free radicals is oxygen," explains the National Cancer Institute, "when an oxygen molecule (O_2) becomes electrically charged or "radicalized" it tries to steal electrons from other molecules, causing damage to the DNA and other molecules. Over time, such damage may become irreversible and lead to disease including cancer."[10]

Antioxidants scavenge for free radicals and stabilize them by either absorbing their extra unstable energy electron, or lending them a spare. Carotenoids, unlike other antioxidants that require regeneration after such exchanges, are exceptionally stable because they can transmute their electron exchanges as heat, allowing them to "quench" multiple free radicals until they are bled dry of their pigment.[11] But before you go out and stock up on beta-carotene pills (which can be toxic if you OD on them), consider that numerous findings conclude "little overall benefit" from antioxidant pills; whereas other studies indicate that folks who eat a plethora of antioxidant rich food "have a lower risk of many diseases.[12] It's like nature is shouting out the answer to our ills with a brilliant rainbow of colored fruits and veggies!

In addition, fall fruits and veggies also contain copious amounts of vitamin C, fiber, minerals and carbohydrates useful to the body's natural increase in caloric consumption at this time of year. In times of yore, it made perfect sense to eat the foods that came into season in the fall (and then hoard them for the winter) because they were the only foods around! Nowadays, just about every food grown in the world is available at any time of year for the right price. Nevertheless, a 2008 study which compared the vitamin C content of broccoli crowns grown in May versus those plucked in the fall, found the out-of-season broccoli to have nearly 50% LESS vitamin C than broccoli harvested during the fall, so it would appear that "seasonality matters" when it comes to maximizing nutrition.[13] Isn't it funny how it takes a modern discovery to reconfirm our scientific faith in the inherent wisdom of the ancient, intuitive cycles of nature? And here you thought candied yams were just a Thanksgiving tradition...

MACADAMIA NUT MYLK

1 c. macadamia nuts
1/4 c. sunflower seeds
1/4 c. pumpkin seeds
2 T. raw honey or coconut nectar
1/2 t. ground vanilla bean
2 pinches sea salt
4 1/4 c. filtered water

Soak the nuts & seeds 4-8 hours to sprout, then drain and rinse. Juice the sprouted nuts & seeds through a champion juicer with the 4 c. water <u>OR</u> blend them with just 1 c. water until smooth before blending in the other 3 cups. Strain the mixture through a thin weave sieve. Save the "nut mylk" in a quart sized jar & add the rest of the ingredients. Shake well! Use the leftover "nut pulp" for the Country Fair S'nutty!

COUNTRY FAIR S'NUTTY

In a cuisinart, whip the "nut pulp" till smooth with the following ingredients:

2 T. lemon juice
1 T. nutritional yeast
1/2 t. sea salt
1 clove garlic, minced
1/4 t. Bragg's Liquid Aminos

Roll your whipped S'nutty into 1" balls and layer them in a clean 16 oz. jar with the following ingredients:

1/3 c. olive oil
1 T. green onion, sliced
1 1/2 T. parsley, minced
1 t. fresh ground black pepper
1 t. rubbed sage
1/4 t. each thyme & rosemary

The revolution of SLOW FOOD has developed in response to the prolif-eration of fast food restaurants around the globe, and seeks to reconnect the dots between yummy local food, environmental sustainability, and traditional cuisines.[14] While few of the recipes in this book will feel "traditional" per se, their prepara-tion does present a hands-on experience, in the sense that any decent homemade meal takes time to prepare. Reconnecting with the earth that grows your food and the inner workings of a meal is really just a means of getting back in touch with yourself -- since all the cells in your body rebuild/regenerate from the ingredients in your crisper and pantry. Nevertheless, this endeavor can be viewed as time consuming if you're on a tight schedule or seeking INSTANT GRATIFICATION. Remember: all good things come to those who wait. The mindfulness and attention you put into your food directly translates into SELF-LOVE!

MISO MUCH LOVE TAHINI DRESSING

1/2 c. raw tahini
1/4 c. lemon juice
1 T. flaxseed oil
1 T. unpasteurized miso
2 t. Nama Shoyu
2 1/2 T. ginger, peeled and chopped
1/2 c. water (adding more to thin if needed)

Blend until creamy! Pour in a jar & store!

BLACK OLIVE DRESSING

1/4 c. flaxseed oil   >
1/3 c. olive oil   >   Combine all
1/2 c. lemon juice   >   ingredients in
3 1/2 T. raw coconut nectar   >   a 16 oz. jar.
2 T. Bragg's Liquid Aminos   >   Shake well
3 T. black olives, minced   >   & store for
2 cloves garlic, minced   >   later use.
2 t. smoked sea salt   >
1/4 t. chipotle powder   >
1/4 t. chile powder   >

PRESTO PESTO DRESSING

1/2 c. basil   ✶
3 T. parsley   ✶   Blend all the
1/4 c. pine nuts, soak   ✶   ingredients
1/4 c. olive oil   ✶   together until
2 T. lemon juice   ✶   smooth & creamy!
1/2 t. pink Himalayan salt   ✶   Store in a jar
1/4 t. raw honey   ✶   for later use.
1 clove garlic, minced   ✶
1/4 c. water   ✶
                              ✶

GINGER FLAX DRESSING

1/2 c. lemon juice   #
1/2 c. flaxseed oil   #
3 T. raw coconut nectar   #   Combine all
2 T. Nama Shoyu   #   ingredients
2 T. grated ginger   #   in a jar and
1 T. Bragg's Liquid Aminos   #   shake well!
1 t. umeboshi plum vinegar   #
1 t. toasted sesame oil   #
1 pinch chile powder   #
                              #

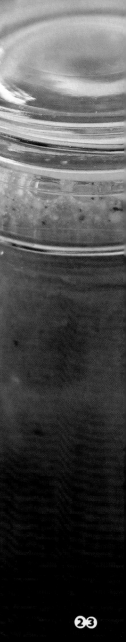

SECRET SAUCES

ARE THE HEART AND VERY *ESSENCE OF CUISINE*. AS A CONCOCTION OF *SPICE & FLAVOR*, A GOOD DRESSING TRANSFORMS THE CANVAS OF UNSUSPECTING VEGGIES INTO A GOURMET MASTERPIECE, EVOKING TASTE & OLFACTORY SENSE MEMORIES THAT CAN TRANSPORT YOU THROUGH TIME AND SPACE. CORPORATE EMPIRES HAVE BEEN BUILT ON SIGNATURE TASTE EXPERIENCES, AND LET'S NOT FORGET THAT CHRISTOPHER COLUMBUS SET SAIL IN 1492 IN SEARCH OF NEW SPICES.[15] THE DRESSINGS ON THIS PAGE ARE YOUR KEY TO BOOSTING YOUR HEALTH & IMMUNITY, SAVING PREP TIME, AND MAKING EVERYTHING DELICIOUS IN THE WEEK TO COME.

TAKE A WALK AROUND YOUR BLOCK AND MAKE A NOTE OF ALL THE EDIBLE FOODS, EVEN IF ONLY THE DANDELIONS, CLOVER AND SORREL GROWING IN THE LAWN GRASS. MANY NEIGHBORS ARE HAPPY TO SHARE THEIR WINDFALLS!

HOLY COW! HOW COME I NEVER NOTICED THE AVOCADO TREE ACROSS THE STREET?

A Case of the Mondays?

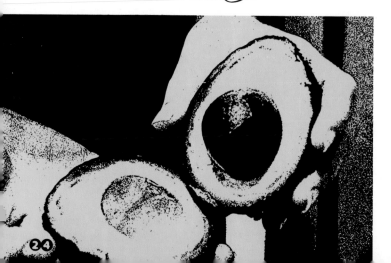

Get wild at home!

IN OUR RADICAL 21st CENTURY LIVES we've traded up the survival card for the industrially farmed opportunity to eat any food we want, any time of year. Foods nowadays are often grown and shipped across the planet to our dinner plates. While this luxury has given us access to super-nutritive supplemental foods -- like goji berries, maca, cacao, yacon, shilajit, seaweeds, medicinal mushrooms, and blue green algaes like spirulina or E3Live -- it's imperative that we base our diet in *seasonal*, *local*, and *wild foods*. Locally grown foods provide you with nutrients uniquely suited to surviving in your immediate surroundings because they've formed subtle cellular adaptations to the same local environmental pressures that also affect YOU; but when it comes to eating foods uniquely adapted to your local neighborhood, nothing tops wild foods in the mineral department. Foods grown without cultivation have mastered the art of surviving against all odds in infertile soils, often despite our attempts to thwart them! As Annie Jubb suggests, look no further than the dandelions on your lawn for immediate proof of the persistent vitality of wild food![16]

One survival strategy wild plants employ is to concentrate nutrients in their tissues, allowing them to continue their respiratory, photosynthetic, and root absorbing functions even when nutrients are scarce.[17] As the nutritional hoarders of the plant world, wild foods are especially rich sources of minerals and phytonutrients. When you ingest wild foods well adapted to the terrain where you live, you are benefitting from their abundant nutrient stores and incorporating their "will to survive" into your own cellular biology.

Another kind of local, wild food is BEE POLLEN, which is harvested by bees from the pollen of flowering plants. Considered throughout the ages to be a panacea for good health, bee pollen contains all the essential nutrients required for sustaining life (trace elements, carotenoids, vitamins, and an abundance of amino acids, essential fatty acids, coenzymes, lots of protein, etc.), as well as some extra "bee magic" science still doesn't fully understand.[18] Bee pollen is effective for correcting malnutrition, fostering longevity, regulating cholesterol, improving intestinal function, boosting memory, endurance & immunity -- it also helps prevent cancer, as well as seasonal allergies![19] According to Steven Schechter, N.D., director of the Natural Healing Institute, bee pollen has even been shown to combat radiation sickness![20]

If you doubt the ability of bee pollen to work wonders, consider an article published in 1948 by the Journal of the National Cancer Institute. In his article, Dr. William Robinson describes an experiment performed on mice specially bred to develop cancerous tumors. According to Dr. Robinson, the mice developed tumors anywhere from 18 to 57 weeks of age, "with an average appearance at 33 weeks. Tumor incidence was 100 percent." Dr. Robinson divided the mice into two groups, one which was fed the usual mice food, and the other which received the same food plus an additional supplement of "bee-gathered" pollen. The outcome was startling: in addition to an overall delay in the development of tumors, seven mice in the pollen fed group remained free of tumors at 56 to 62 weeks of age when the study ended.[21]

Conversely, HYBRID FOODS have been crossbred for sweetness, shelf life & appearance. According to longevity expert David Wolfe, the elevated sugar content in hybrid foods forces your body to leach heavy minerals from your bones in order to buffer all the extra glucose in your bloodstream that isn't completely processed by your liver & pancreas.[22] Hybrid foods either don't produce seeds or produce seeds that are incapable of surviving well on their own in nature. If a hybrid seed does survive, it doesn't replicate its hybridized traits (whereas HEIRLOOM SEEDS will replicate their traits one generation to the next). Hybridization also compromises a plant's mineral balance (when you're spoon fed fertilizers, why bother stockpiling mineral reserves?).[23] Common hybrid foods include: carrots, beets, corn, wheat, oranges, bananas, soy, rice, and potatoes... so eat them with awareness! If these are all your favorite foods, don't feel like you have to nix them completely, just apply your focus on ADDING MORE MINERAL RICH FOODS to your diet!

SELF-LOVE CEREAL

1 apple, shredded
2/3 c. assorted berries, fresh and frozen
1/4 c. untoasted coconut shreds/flakes
1 T. dried cranberries, raisins, or Inca berries
1 T. goji berries
1/2 T. pumpkin seeds
5 macadamias, pecans, or walnuts
3 dashes cinnamon
1/4 t. lemon zest/grated peel

Put all ingredients in a bowl (berries on top),
and douse with:

3/4 c. Macadamia Nut Mylk (p.20)

IF YOU HAVE MORE TIME AND $$$...
Try sneaking in some superfood supplements
to really fortify your nutrition. Boost your
cereal with:

1 T. cacao nibs
2 t. ground flax or chia seeds
1 t. bee pollen
1/2 t. maca powder
1/2 t. Crystal Manna Flakes or Spirulina Manna

Supplements are worth the investment. Most
will last you several months if they're kept in
the fridge!

MACA-BEE-POLLEN-SPIRULINA-CACAO-GOJI

IS A LITTLE 21ST CENTURY HYMN FOR EVERYONE'S BACK POCKET. SING IT TO YOURSELF AS YOU SPRINKLE THEM ON EVERYTHING! *MACA* BALANCES YOUR ENDOCRINE SYSTEM, SUPPORTS THE THYROID, AND BOOSTS ENERGY & FERTILITY.[24] *BEE POLLEN* FROM LOCAL BEE KEEPERS CAN "INOCULATE" YOUR IMMUNE SYSTEM AGAINST POLLEN ALLERGIES. THE BLUE PIGMENT PHYCOCYANIN FOUND WITHIN THE SINGLE-CELLED *SPIRULINA* ORGANISM AIDS WITH THE FORMATION OF NEUROTRANSMITTERS IN THE BRAIN; WHILE THE GAMMA-LINOLENIC ACID IN SPIRULINA ACTS AS A NOTORIOUS IMMUNITY BOOSTER.[25] SHAZZIE AND DAVID WOLFE HAVE REFERRED TO *CACAO* TO "NATURE'S PROZAC" BECAUSE IT PROVIDES THE BRAIN WITH NEUROTRANSMITTERS LIKE ANADAMIDE, SEROTONIN & DOPAMINE, AS WELL AS PHENYLETHYLLAMINE (PEA): A SUBSTANCE THAT "INCREASES THE ACTIVITY OF NEUROTRANSMITTERS" AND PROMOTES FEELINGS OF LOVE, JOY AND WELLBEING.[26] LASTLY, *GOJI BERRIES* ARE HISTORICALLY EXCELLENT FOR OVERALL HEALTH AND LONGEVITY, AS PROVEN BY LI QING YUEN, WHO ATE THEM EVERY DAY AND LIVED TO BE 252 YEARS OLD![27] FERTILITY, HEALTH AND SURVIVAL IN A MECHA-URBANIZED WORLD DEPEND ON SUPER NUTRITION!

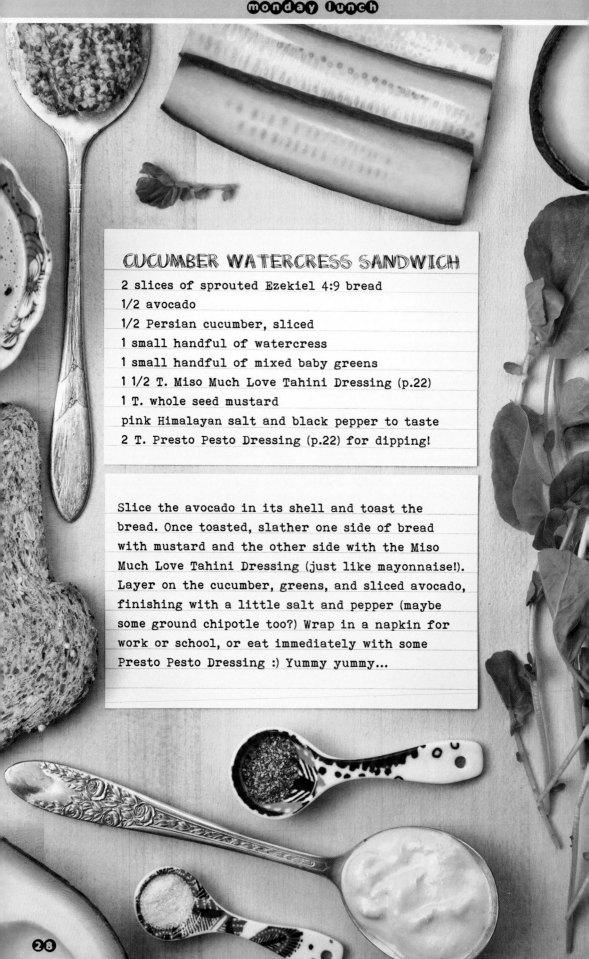

CUCUMBER WATERCRESS SANDWICH

2 slices of sprouted Ezekiel 4:9 bread
1/2 avocado
1/2 Persian cucumber, sliced
1 small handful of watercress
1 small handful of mixed baby greens
1 1/2 T. Miso Much Love Tahini Dressing (p.22)
1 T. whole seed mustard
pink Himalayan salt and black pepper to taste
2 T. Presto Pesto Dressing (p.22) for dipping!

Slice the avocado in its shell and toast the
bread. Once toasted, slather one side of bread
with mustard and the other side with the Miso
Much Love Tahini Dressing (just like mayonnaise!).
Layer on the cucumber, greens, and sliced avocado,
finishing with a little salt and pepper (maybe
some ground chipotle too?) Wrap in a napkin for
work or school, or eat immediately with some
Presto Pesto Dressing :) Yummy yummy...

AVOCADOS ARE 85% FAT; BUT THE FATS CONTAINED IN AVOCADO ARE NOTHING TO BE AFRAID OF. MUCH OF IT COMES IN THE FORM OF PHYTOSTEROLS, WHICH ARE **ANTI-INFLAMMATORY** AND VERY GOOD FOR FOLKS WITH ARTHRITIS.[28] IN ADDITION, AVOCADOS ARE RICH IN **OLEIC ACID**, A HEALTHY **MONOUNSATURATED FATTY ACID** THAT HELPS THE BODY CREATE MORE GOOD **HDL** CHOLESTEROL, WHICH IN TURN HELPS TRANSPORT THE BAD **LDL** CHOLESTEROL TO YOUR LIVER SO IT CAN BE BROKEN DOWN. OLEIC ACID ALSO INCREASES THE ABSORPTION OF THE FAT SOLUBLE ANTIOXIDANT CAROTENOIDS LYCOPENE AND BETA-CAROTENE BY **200-400%!**[29] YEP, THAT MEANS YOU ABSORB MORE ANTIOXIDANT POWER FROM YOUR TOMATOES, CARROTS AND LEAFY GREENS WHEN YOU EAT THEM WITH SOME AVOCADO.

BLACK TRUFFLE RICE

1 1/3 c. cooked wild rice (see below)
1/2 c. avocado, cubed
2 t. parsley, minced
1 t. umeboshi plum vinegar
1/2 t. flax oil
1/4 t. truffle oil
2 pinches smoked sea salt

To have enough rice for this recipe and
lunch tomorrow, rinse 1/2 c. wild rice
and bring it to boil with 3 c. water.

Simmer for 1 hour, or until the kernels
split open. Once cooked, prepare the
recipe and set aside half for tomorrow's
lunch.

Press tonight's portion into a form
(like a 1 c. measuring cup), and adorn
with the Smokey Shallot/Shitakes below.

SMOKY SHALLOTS/SHITAKES

1/2 c. shitake mushroom, sliced
3 T. shallot, sliced thin
1 clove garlic, minced
1 t. olive oil
1/4 t. rosemary
1/4 t. black pepper
1 pinch smoked sea salt
1 pinch ground chipotle pepper
1 dash umeboshi plum vinegar
1 dash Nama Shoyu

Heat the oil in a skillet and
add the rosemary, garlic, and
shallots, stirring a few times.
Then add the shitakes, and
sauté for about 45 seconds.
Add spices, and dash with ume
vinegar and nama shoyu; serve
immediately over the Black
Truffle Rice with:

1 big handful mixed baby greens
2 T. Presto Pesto Dressing (p.20)

Enjoy!

LONG GRAIN WILD RICE IS THE SEED OF AN AQUATIC GRASS
THAT GROWS IN SMALL LAKES AND SLOW MOVING STREAMS NATIVE TO THE GREAT LAKES REGION OF NORTH AMERICA. ITS RISE IN POPULARITY HAS EXPANDED ITS CULTIVATION, BUT IN SOME PLACES IT'S STILL TRADITIONALLY THRESHED BY THE OBJIWA TRIBE WHO CONSIDER IT A SACRED RITUAL TO HARVEST THE "MANOOMIN" BY GENTLY KNOCKING THE MATURE SEEDS FROM THE **FLOWERING PLANT HEADS** INTO THEIR CANOES. HIGH IN PROTEIN, IMMUNE BOOSTING **LYSINE**, POTASSIUM, PHOSPHORUS, & B1, B2, B3. WILD RICE ALSO CONTAINS AN AMINO ACID CALLED **LEUCINE**, WHICH HELPS REGULATE BLOOD SUGAR LEVELS, THE PRODUCTION OF GROWTH HORMONES, WOUND REPAIR, AND THE PROTEIN SYNTHESIS THAT BOTH BUILDS AND PRESERVES MUSCLE.[30,31] LEUCINE IS ABUNDANT IN **FLESH, DAIRY,** AND **PROTEIN FOODS** (LENTILS, SESAME, PEANUTS). SUPPLEMENTARY INTAKE IS ESSENTIAL, BECAUSE OUR BODIES DON'T NATURALLY PRODUCE IT.

4

I DIDN'T KNOW YOU COULD COOK SOUP *WITHOUT* COOKING IT! *WHAT FUN!*

And so it came to pass that Ingrid cherished investing in herself and the pleasure of a carefully warmed meal.

BE SURE TO KEEP *THE FLAME ON LOW* SINCE YOU DON'T WANT IT ANY HOTTER THAN *108 DEGREES!!!*

FRONT

LOW   HI   LITE

Strip away the veil of civilization and you will observe that all forms of plant, animal and insect life, which have evolved on earth over the last 2 billion years, did so without the aid of toasters or microwave ovens. That's right, up and down the food chain, life eats life in its raw, uncooked, and enzymatically active state. Amazingly, the same enzymes that facilitate the growth of any living thing, also serve as the breakdown crew for its eventual decomposition. So when it comes to the daily phenomena of ingesting nutrients for the purpose of feeding all the tissues in your body, enzymes play a lead role in disassembling your breakfast into chemical structures small enough to be absorbed by your hungry cells.[32] Nothing in nature wants to work harder than it has to, so it makes sense that an organism's digestive process would capitalize on the inherent biodegradative properties that enzymes lend to the legwork of breaking down nutrients.

All living cells produce enzymes, which have been described as little protein molecules that work both chemically and biologically to catalyze reactions and otherwise transform molecular substrates into their smaller components. Despite their chemical applications, enzymes in a biological setting have often been described as "life energy" itself.[33] According to Stephen Blauer, former Director of the Hippocrates Health Institute, "without the life energy of enzymes we would be nothing more than a pile of lifeless chemical substances -- vitamins, minerals, water, and proteins. In both maintaining health and in healing, enzymes and only enzymes do the actual work. They are what we call in metabolism, the body's labor force."[34] Enzymes have been documented as catalyzing over 4,000 different chemical reactions, as well as nearly every function within the human body. But not all enzymes act the same way -- specific enzymes catalyze specific molecules: lipase enzymes catalyze fats, amylases catalyze starches, and proteases catalyze proteins. Cells produce enzymes to govern their metabolism, and these enzymes usually correlate with the composition of their surrounding cellular structures. For example, it has been thoroughly observed in scientific communities that "wherever the chemist finds fat in nature, he also finds the enzyme lipase."[35] In the case of the olive, lipase is responsible for facilitating the growth and maintenance of the olive's fats, as well as the eventual deconstruction of those fats!

Any food in its raw, unheated state is enzymatically alive and capable of decomposing itself if left to rot under a tree or neglected in your crisper drawer; or if eaten, of making an enzymatic contribution towards its own digestion.[36] Unfortunately, enzymes begin to wear out and expire around 105 degrees, and cannot survive sustained temperatures above 118 degrees for very long, so any food that has been roasted, sautéed, baked, boiled, microwaved, canned, fried, pasteurized, or otherwise denatured by heat, has been rendered enzymatically inert and is thus incapable of digesting itself. Because enzymes are integral to the digestive process -- how else do you transform lasagna into something your cells can absorb? -- enzymatically inert food requires a sort of jumper cable from your body's enzyme reserves. While some would argue the human body naturally produces digestive enzymes all the time, evidence suggests the demand of enzymatically inert food overworks and enlarges your pancreas by forcing it to confiscate your body's metabolic enzymes and repurpose them into digestive enzymes. Not only is this potentially harmful to your pancreas, but it appears to create an "enzyme labor shortage" in the rest of your organs and tissues.[37]

In a decade long study performed on 900 cats by Francis Marion Pottenger, Jr. from 1932-1942, it was observed that cats fed a diet of raw milk and meat scraps lived normal healthy lives and reproduced indefinitely, while those fed a diet of cooked & processed foods suffered progressively from one generation to the next from malnutrition, deformities, hypothyroidism, malocclusion, allergies, skin disorders, diminished life span, infertility, still births, and eventually sterility -- leaving no fourth generation of cats to study.[38] While Dr. Pottenger never compared his studies in animal nutrition with his studies of human nutrition, he did say: "While no attempt will be made to correlate the changes in the animals studied with malformations found in humans, the similarity is so obvious that parallel pictures will suggest themselves."[39]

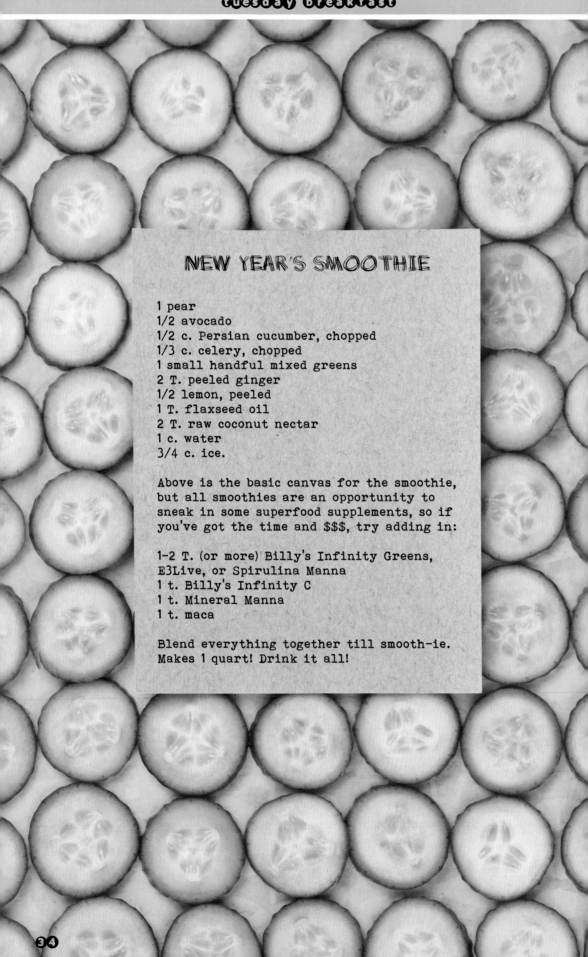

NEW YEAR'S SMOOTHIE

1 pear
1/2 avocado
1/2 c. Persian cucumber, chopped
1/3 c. celery, chopped
1 small handful mixed greens
2 T. peeled ginger
1/2 lemon, peeled
1 T. flaxseed oil
2 T. raw coconut nectar
1 c. water
3/4 c. ice.

Above is the basic canvas for the smoothie,
but all smoothies are an opportunity to
sneak in some superfood supplements, so if
you've got the time and $$$, try adding in:

1-2 T. (or more) Billy's Infinity Greens,
E3Live, or Spirulina Manna
1 t. Billy's Infinity C
1 t. Mineral Manna
1 t. maca

Blend everything together till smooth-ie.
Makes 1 quart! Drink it all!

KLAMATH LAKE BLUE GREEN ALGAE -- OTHERWISE

KNOWN AS *APHANIZOMENON FLOS-AQUAE* OR "SUPER BLUE GREEN ALGAE" -- IS CONSIDERED BY MANY TO BE THE MOTHER OF ALL SUPERFOODS. IT'S WILD HARVESTED FROM THE KLAMATH LAKES, WHERE IT FEEDS ON THE LAKE'S NUTRIENT DENSE SEDIMENT. FRESH HARVESTED *AFA* CONTAINS 65 DIFFERENT VITAMINS, MINERALS AND ENZYMES IN A BIOAVAILABLE FORMAT FOR EASY DOWNLOADING INTO YOUR ENDOCRINE, IMMUNE, NERVOUS, GASTROINTESTINAL, AND CARDIOVASCULAR SYSTEMS![40] *AFA*, AS WELL AS BLUE GREEN ALGAE SPIRULINA AND GREEN ALGAE CHLORELLA, ARE THE SINGLE MOST IMPORTANT SUPPLEMENTS TO ADD TO YOUR DIET. THEY HAVE BEEN CONSUMED BY PEOPLE FOR THOUSANDS OF YEARS, SO THEIR COMEBACK IS MUCH TO BE EXPECTED.[41] FURTHERMORE, RECENT STUDIES HAVE SHOWN SPIRULINA AND *AFA* ARE IMMEDIATELY EFFECTIVE IN PROMOTING GENERAL IMMUNITY BY MOBILIZING THE "TUMORCIDAL" EFFORTS OF "NATURAL KILLER CELLS," WHICH MIGRATE INTO TISSUES AND SCAVENGE FOR CANCEROUS OR VIRALLY INFECTED CELLS, INITIATING THEIR CELL DEATH PROGRAM.[42,43] GREEN IS GOLDEN WHEN IT COMES TO HEALTH, SO DRINK UP AND SAVOR EVERY LAST DROP!

KITCHEN SINK SALAD

2 c. mixed baby greens
2/3 c. Black Truffled Rice (p.30)
3" burdock root, peeled & julienned
1/4 c. golden beet, shredded
1/4 c. Live Zing or Wild Brine sauerkraut
1/4 c. Country Fair S'nutty (p.20)
3 T. Black Olive Dressing (p.22)
1 T. green onion, sliced
1 small tuft of sprouts
1 radish, sliced

Toss the greens with 2 T. Black Olive
Dressing & arrange the other ingredients
on top in a smorgasbord fashion. Garnish
with the remainder of the dressing, and:

1 T. parsley minced
1-2 pinches ground chipotle

Happy noshing!

BURDOCK ROOT GROWS ALL OVER THE WORLD LIKE A WEED. IN AYURVEDIC MEDICINE BURDOCK IS USED TO TREAT SKIN DISORDERS AND PURIFY THE BLOOD, AS IT IS ALSO RICH IN IRON, MANGANESE, SILICON, ZINC, CALCIUM AND PHOSPHORUS. IT HAS A NEUTRAL PH BALANCE & CONTAINS ANTI-INFLAMMATORY PROPERTIES.[44] AS IF THAT WEREN'T ENOUGH, THE HUMBLE BURDOCK ALSO STIMULATES THE FLOW OF BILE AND DIGESTIVE JUICES, AND CONTAINS THE PRE-BIOTIC INULIN, WHICH FEEDS THE FRIENDLY "PROBIOTIC" BACTERIA IN YOUR INTESTINES HELPING THEM GROW AND FLOURISH.[45]

MISO MUSHROOM STEW

2/3 c. finely chopped mushrooms (portobella, shitake, oyster)
2 Tbs. maitake mushrooms (fresh or dried/soaked) – OPTIONAL!

Marinate the mushrooms in: 1 T. olive oil, 1 1/2 t. Nama Shoyu, and 1 t. balsamic vinegar. While the 'shrooms are marinating, bring 1 c. of water almost to a simmer on the stove. Turn off the heat and let the following steep for 5 minutes:

1/3 c. carrot, sliced thin
1/3 c. stalk celery, sliced thin
1/3 c. summer squash, sliced thin
1/4 c. Jerusalem artichoke, sliced thin
2 T. shallots, chopped fine
2 cloves garlic, minced

Then add the marinated mushrooms along with:

2 1/2 T. unpasteurized white miso paste mixed with 1/2 c. water
1/2 c. chard, minced
1 1/2 T. parsley, minced
1 t. smoked sea salt
1/2 t. sage and rosemary
1/2 t. black pepper
1/4 to 1/2 t. truffle oil – OPTIONAL!

Lastly, mix and mash it all together and reheat if needed until "bath-water" hot, but no hotter than 108 degrees if you want to preserve the beneficial enzymes! Serve with Country Fair S'nutty (p.20) and sprouts on a slice of toasted Manna or Ezekiel 4:9 bread!

BETA GLUCAN IS A POWERFUL POLYSACCHARIDE THAT STIMULATES THE IMMUNE SYSTEM TO RALLY AN ATTACK AGAINST CANCER CELLS ON A CELLULAR LEVEL, SLOWING THEIR GROWTH.[46] SCIENTISTS AROUND THE WORLD ARE CURRENTLY STUDYING THE CANCER FIGHTING PROPERTIES OF BETA GLUCAN, WHICH IS READILY FOUND IN SEVERAL MUSHROOMS, BUT MOST NOTABLY PRESENT IN MAITAKE MUSHROOMS. SO PRIZED FOR THEIR MEDICINAL PROPERTIES, MAITAKE MUSHROOMS WERE WORTH THEIR WEIGHT IN SILVER IN ANCIENT TIMES AND WERE NAMED THE "DANCING MUSHROOM" BECAUSE PEOPLE WOULD LITERALLY DANCE FOR JOY WHEN THEY FOUND THEM![47] MUSHROOMS WERE ONCE BELIEVED TO HAVE NO NUTRITIONAL VALUE, BUT WE NOW KNOW THEY ARE RICH IN B-VITAMINS, PHOSPHORUS, SODIUM, SELENIUM AND POTASSIUM,

Hump Day

A change of taste

While many tastes are acquired, we now know that our palate can be influenced by the foods our mothers eat while they're pregnant, as well as by the foods we are socialized to eat as toddlers -- whether they're spicy, bland, or the excitotoxins of processed food.[48,49] For those unaware, excitotoxins are substances such as MSG, aspartame, yeast extract, textured protein, soy protein extract, hydrolyzed vegetable protein, generically labeled "spices," and artificial/natural flavors, which are added to make food taste better.[50] When they get to the brain, elevated levels of these excitotoxins cause brain neurons to fire abnormally and experience "excitotoxicity," during which they are literally "excited to death."[51] A growing body of research suggests that excitotoxins play a role in all kinds of neurological disorders and neurodegenerative diseases like Parkinson's and Alzheimer's.[52]

To provide some insight into the chemical composition of artificial flavorings, consider that "artifical strawberry flavoring" can include more ingredients than whatever it's been added too. As Eric Schlosser cleverly disclosed in *Fast Food Nation*, the artificial strawberry flavor found in most milk shakes contains a very long list of chemically derived ingredients like "methyl benzoate," "anethol," "y-undecalactone," "benzyl isobutyrate," "hydroxyphenyl-2-butanone (10 percent solution in alcohol)," "isobutyl butyrate," "4-methylacetophenone," and "methyl naphthyl ketone," just to name a few.[53] Toss in a little solvent and a few essential oils, and you've got yourself a patented taste sensation! If you think *natural flavors* are any better, think again. So-called natural flavors often contain all the same isolated chemicals that artificial flavors do, they're just derived using different methods.[54]

As depressing as this may be, never fear! A quick scan of a product's ingredients can help you avoid such chemical additives in the future. And even if your palate has been inadvertently seasoned towards the destructive thrill of unhealthy foods, THERE IS STILL HOPE! You can learn to crave good things by using your brain to prime your tongue by reading and learning as much about the nutritional benefits of whatever healthy food you'd like to enjoy. Take flaxseed oil as an example. Study up on the essential fatty acids found in flaxseed oil and identify something in your own health that would benefit from it -- like your joints, your skin, or your memory. Then, the next time you taste flaxseed oil, remind yourself of everything wonderful you've learned about it, and know that your memory, joints and skin are all loving the EFA's! In this way, you can retrain yourself to identify the earthy, medicinal tastes of whole foods as *full-bodied flavors*, and even start to crave them, as well as their positive effects on your health. Sounds crazy, but it works. Try it out!

Remember: just because you can put something in your mouth doesn't mean you should eat it. Humans are "dietary opportunists" -- we follow the path of least resistance, tending to eat whatever is easiest when we're hungry. The fast food craze is evidence of this, as is the natural world. A tree loaded with ripe fruit puts up no resistance to the hungers of humankind, nor does a patch of wild celery, tender greens, or a windfall of nuts on the ground. Eggs, small birds and hand caught fish are a little harder to come by. More challenging still, is hunting down a large wild gazelle that has genetically evolved to evade predators, butchering and finally cooking it! Take into consideration the tool-making needed to compensate for your lack of tiger-claws, and this ordeal becomes a heroic effort. In my opinion, human beings are most physically adapted to eat whole, herbivorous foods that require the least amount of effort to find and prepare, and the ratio to which other foods are eaten should be in accordance with the level of difficulty required to forage them. When you eat an apple, you are participating in the apple tree's reproductive process. The tree has adapted its fruit to be sweet and enticing to INSURE THAT IT'S EATEN, so that more apple trees can sprout from the bitter, undigested seeds tucked inside the tossed core.[55]

So the next time you eat an apple, just know that you're not hurting the tree. YOU'RE MAKING LOVE TO IT.

CURRIED BREAKFAST OATS

1/2 c. rolled oats
1 1/4 c. water
2 t. coconut oil
1 1/2 t. Bragg's Liquid Aminos
1/2 t. nutritional yeast
1/2 t. curry
1/4 t. sesame oil
1/4 t. black pepper
1/4 t. cumin
1/4 t. turmeric
1 pinch each chipotle & paprika

Bring water to a boil and add the oats.
Simmer on low until the water is gone.
Stir in the oils & spices. Serve with:

4" stalk celery, diced
1 radish, julienned
1/3 c. apple, shredded
1/4 c. chard, minced
1 T. green onion, sliced
1 T. parsley, minced
1 t. sesame seeds

Douse with 2-3 T. Ginger Flax Dressing
(p.22) for extra juiciness!

OATS ARE SO UNDER APPRECIATED. NOT ONLY ARE THEY HIGH IN *SELENIUM*, *MANGANESE* AND *SILICON*, KEY MINERALS FOR HEALTHY SKIN, HAIR & NAILS, BUT THEY ALSO CONTAIN THE GREAT *BETA-GLUCAN* AS WELL! THAT'S RIGHT, IN ADDITION TO ITS ANTI-CANCER PROPERTIES, THE MERE DAILY ESSENCE OF BETA-GLUCAN FOUND IN A SINGLE BOWL OF OATMEAL CONCLUSIVELY REDUCES OVERALL CHOLESTEROL LEVELS BY **8-23%!**[56,57] IF THAT WEREN'T EXCITING ENOUGH, OATS ALSO CONTAIN COMPOUNDS CALLED *AVENANTHRAMIDES*, WHICH *SPECIFI-CALLY* THWART FREE RADICALS FROM DAMAGING *LDL (GOOD) CHOLESTEROL*.[58] OATS ARE *HIGHLY BENEFICIAL* TO THOSE CHALLENGED WITH DIABETES BECAUSE THEY'RE A SLOW BURNING CAR-BOHYDRATE. THIS MEANS THE BODY CAN MOTOR THOUGH THEM ALL DAY LONG WITHOUT A SERIOUS SPIKE IN BLOOD SUGAR. SOME RAW FOODISTS LIKE TO SOAK AND SPROUT OATS GROATS JUST LIKE OTHER GRAINS. ONCE SOFT, THEY BLEND THEM WITH DATES AND CINNAMON. YOU COULD DO THIS TOO IF YOU WANTED, BUT TRY BLENDING THEM WITH THE SAVORY SPICES ON THE OPPOSITE PAGE AND THEN *CAREFULLY WARMING* THEM ON THE STOVE (BEFORE MIXING IN THE FRESH INGREDIENTS) TO HEAT UP THOSE CHILLY FALL MORNINGS.

YE GOOD OLE COLLARD WRAP

1-2 collard leaves
1/3 c. Country Fair S'nutty (p.20)
1/4 avocado
1/2 Persian cucumber, sliced
1 small tomato, sliced
1 BIG handful of mixed baby greens
1 small tuft of sprouts
2 T. Live Zing or Wild Brine sauerkraut
2-3 T. Black Olive Dressing (p.22)

ASSEMBLY INSTRUCTIONS:
Cut the thick stalk off the collard leaves, and overlap them to create a circular wrap. Layer in the S'nutty, sauerkraut, avo, cuke, tomato, sprouts and greens. Drizzle with Black Olive Dressing, roll up and eat! If you're packing this lunch "to-go," then assemble your wrap over a sheet of saran and/or waxed paper <u>and keep the dressing on the side</u> for ease of transport!

COLLARDS ARE IN THE BRASSICA FAMILY OF VEGETABLES, ALONG WITH KALE, BROCCOLI AND CABBAGE, AND THUS ARE RICH IN BIODYNAMIC COMPOUNDS LIKE DIINDOLYLMETHANE (DIM) AND SULPHORAPHANE. WORD ON THE STREET IS THAT THE NATIONAL CANCER INSTITUTE HAS BEGUN CLINICAL TRIALS WITH DIM AS A TREATMENT FOR VARIOUS FORMS OF CANCER, SINCE IT HAS EXHIBITED ANTI-ANGIOGENESIS, ANTI-INFLAMMATORY, ANTI-VIRAL, ANTI-BACTERIAL, ANTI-CANCEROUS, AND APOPTOSIS PROPERTIES WHEN APPLIED TOWARDS PROTEINS IN LABORATORY STUDIES.[59,60] WOW! A DARK GREEN LEAFY VEGETABLE, COLLARDS ARE ABUNDANT IN CHLOROPHYLL AND BIOAVAILABLE AMINO ACIDS WITH A "PROTIEN QUALITY" SCORE OF 94 OUT OF 100.[61] SO EAT UP AND SAVOR YOUR ACCESS TO ALL THE INCREDIBLE PROPERTIES OF A SIMPLE COLLARD LEAF!

AUTUMN ROOT SALAD SUSHI

✳✳✳ You can make this recipe with your grater or with a champion juicer ✳✳✳

1 large carrot
1/2 small yam
1/3 c. celery, diced
1 T. ginger, minced
1 T. shallot, minced
1 T. parsley, minced
1 t. cilantro, minced
1/2 t. nutritional yeast
1/2 t. dried dill weed
2 1/2 T. Miso Much Love Tahini Dressing (p.22)
2 t. Bragg's Liquid Aminos

Peel the carrot and yam and either fine shred them <u>OR</u> push them through a Champion juicer without the juicing plate on (don't forget the blade shield). Fold in the remaining ingredients and <u>set aside half for tomorrow's sandwich.</u> Then prep your rolling ingredients:

1 sheet of nori, cut in half
1/2 persian cucumber, julienned
2" burdock, julienned
1/2 avocado, sliced
1 BIG handful of mixed baby greens
2 T. pickled ginger
10 long sprouts (optional)
2 T. Miso Much Love Tahini Dressing
2 T. Live Zing Salad or Wild Brine sauerkraut

Divide and stack the rolling veggies along with the Autumn Root Salad over the two half sheets of nori. Roll them into fancy cones or little burritos.

Serve with the sauerkraut and dip in the Miso Much Love Tahini Dressing for added flavor!

SEAWEEDS ARE RICH IN VITAMIN K, B VITAMINS, MANGANESE, ORGANIC SODIUM, AND LIGNANS - PHYTONUTRIENTS WHICH HAVE BEEN SHOWN TO INHIBIT ANGIOGENESIS (THE PROCESS BY WHICH TUMORS GROW AND SPREAD TO OTHER PARTS OF THE BODY THROUGH THE BLOODSTREAM).[62] SEA VEGGIES ALSO OFFER THE HIGHEST SOURCE OF BIOAVAILABLE IODINE IN NATURE, WHICH CAN BE GREAT FOR SUPPLYING YOUR THYROID -- AS WELL AS EVERY OTHER CELL IN YOUR BODY -- THE IODINE NEEDED TO STAY HEALTHY AND FUNCTION PROPERLY.[63] WHILE RESEARCH SUGGESTS A LINK BETWEEN LOW IODINE LEVELS AND BREAST CANCER,[64] NUMEROUS OTHER STUDIES HAVE PROVEN THAT SEA VEGGIES ARE ANTI-CARCINOGENIC, AND INTERFERE WITH ESTROGEN SYNTHESIS IN FAT CELLS THE SAME WAY CHE-MOTHERAPY DOES, MAKING THEM PARTICULARLY BENEFICIAL FOR WOMEN CHALLENGED

Confronted by a surplus of neighborhood lemons, Ingrid felt inspired to mix up a pitcher of fresh lemonade.

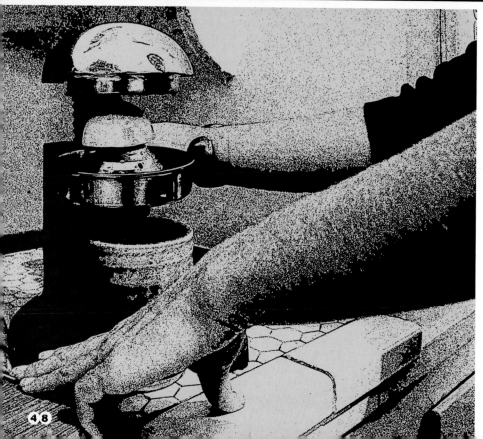

Thursdays Come and Go...

HOW DO YOU FEED A CELL? It's rather ridiculous to imagine a greasy spoon restaurant full of cells at checkered tables and booths, slurping up little plates of ravioli, borscht, or dim sum... but the truth is that it happens everyday all over the world. As an organism of the human variety, you are a *continuous organization* of cells working collectively to create and sustain the experience of the body you live in. Every time you sit down to have a meal you are taking all your billions of cells out to eat all at once... or rather, *they* are taking *you* out! You represent the unified effort of all those billions of cells to seek out food, chew it up, digest it, and absorb as many sugars, fats, proteins, vitamins, minerals, phytosterols, polysacharrides, fatty acids, etc. as possible to maintain and regenerate your very physical existence - which is nothing short of AMAZING! Through the catabolic process of digestion, food molecules are broken down and converted into cellular energy, and HEAT is generated as a byproduct of this energy exchange.[67] Not only is this "heat" an essential component in the seasonal snuggling so prevalent this time of year, but it also helps maintain the optimal temperature for the happy enzymatic activity that governs all your metabolic processes.[68]

If enzymes are catalysts or "the labor force" in the elaborate biochemical ballet of digestion, then your physical body is the dancehall in which it all takes place. From the lips to the anus, the digestive tract (or "alimentary canal") is fundamentally a 30-foot muscular tube designed to physically propel foodstuffs through the body with the action of "peristalsis."[69] Along the way teeth, saliva, digestive enzymes & acids -- plus friendly "probiotic" bacteria living in the gut -- work in tandem with the food's own enzymes (if raw) to pulverize, denature, and otherwise *crack* the code of nutritional data before it gets absorbed through the porous walls of the intestines and filtered into your bloodstream. Once in the bloodstream, these basic chemical structures of nutrition circulate through all your tissues and your hungry cells "download" them by absorbing them through their membranes. Magically, the latter part of your alimentary canal is dual-purposed and works as a conduit for eliminating what cannot be assimilated, as well as bodily wastes and toxins.[70] This is how we become what we eat - but really the degree to which you are nourished by your diet is a reflection of what you're able to *absorb*.

In the passion of chomping away on a well crafted meal, it's very easy to dismiss that roughly one third of the digestive process begins in the mouth.[71] Chewing marks your first and ONLY opportunity to maximize your food's *nutritional surface area* through mastication and the infusion of salivary enzymes. Powerful starch busting ALPHA-AMYLASE "PTYALIN" and fat hydrolyzing LINGUAL LIPASE -- secreted by glands under the tongue -- get to work *before* food even reaches your stomach.[72] Now, because that cozy little mucous lined pouch of your stomach is totally devoid of teeth -- that's right, no such thing as "gastric dentata!" -- the longer you chew your food, the more time your salivary enzymes have to work, and the more easily the acid wash of your gastric secretions can flow through whatever you've ingested, preparing it all together into liquid "chyme." Once transformed into chyme, your liquified foodstuffs shuffle down the alimentary canal to your duodenum for a jumper cable of digestive enzymes culled from your pancreas and small intestine. Sufficiently infused with enzymatic activity, the chyme then slithers into the rest of your small intestine and begins the long, slow phase of fermentation and absorption into your bloodstream.[73]

Although CAREFUL CHEWING directly increases the nutrition your cells can absorb, it's much easier said than done.[74,75] Sometimes I catch myself motoring through my salad like a wild animal, pausing only for intermittent gasps of air. Alas, such revelations are opportunities for mindfulness. Slow the conveyor belt to your mouth by putting your fork down between bites, and remember that *the nutrition locked in unchewed, fibrous chunks can't be properly assimilated.* This is one reason why liquid diets and smoothies produce such powerful results - especially if they're CHEWED after they're juiced or blended. The plethora of smoothie recipes in this book exist to support the reality that liquefied foodstuffs provide superior, food-enzyme rich nutrition with a huge surface area of digestibility! **49**

CHOCOCHIA SMOOTHIE

1 c. banana
1/2 c. Persian cucumber, chopped
1/4 c. celery, chopped
1 small handful of greens
2 T. raw cacao powder
2 T. raw coconut nectar
1 T. flaxseed oil
2 t. ground chia seeds
1/4 t. ground vanilla bean
1/8 t. almond extract
1 pinch pink Himalayan salt
3/4 c. water
1/2 c. ice

OPTIONAL SUPPLEMENTS:
1 t. (or more) E3Live, Spirulina Manna, or
Billy's Infinity Greens
1 t. Mineral Manna
1/2 t. maca

Blend everything on high till smooth
and creamy. Garnish with a mint leaf &
a dash of cinnamon. Makes a little more
than 3 cups of chocolately goodness :)

CHIA IS A FLOWERING PLANT IN THE MINT FAMILY THAT GROWS NATIVE TO SOUTH AMERICA. ITS NAME COMES FROM THE NAHUATL WORD "CHIAN." WHICH MEANS "OILY." CHIA SEEDS ARE A HIGH PROTEIN FOOD, RICH IN ANTIOXIDANTS AND MINERALS LIKE PHOSPHORUS, MANGANESE, CALCIUM, POTASSIUM, ZINC, AND SODIUM. CHIA PACKS MORE OMEGA 3 ESSENTIAL FATTY ACID CONTENT THAN ANY OTHER PLANT KNOWN, AND UNLIKE SALMON, CONTAINS ZERO CHOLESTEROL![76] IT'S ALSO SAID THAT CHIA SEEDS INHIBIT THE ABSORPTION OF CALORIES AND SLOW THE RATE AT WHICH CARBOHYDRATES ARE METABOLIZED INTO SUGARS, MAKING THEM ANOTHER BENEFICIAL FOOD FOR THOSE CHALLENGED WITH DIABETES, OR ANYONE LOOKING TO SHED SOME EXTRA POUNDS.[77] AND YES, CHIA SEEDS ARE ALSO USED TO GROW THE HAIR ON "CHIA PETS." AN EXCITING DEMONSTRATION OF THE SPROUTING PROCESS!

GRAND SLAM "DLT" YAMWICH

2 slices of sprouted Ezekiel 4:9 bread
2 leaves romaine, chard, collard or kale
1/2 avocado
1 small tomato, sliced
1/2 Persian cucumber, sliced
4-5 leaves of dulse
1 big tuft of sprouts
Autumn Root Salad from last night (p.46)
2 T. Miso Much Love Tahini Dressing (p.22)
pink salt and pepper to taste

Toast the bread. Slather one side with the
Tahini Dressing and the other with Autumn
Root Salad. Pile the remaining ingredients
on top, and finish with a little salt and
pepper.

Wrap in a cloth napkin for lunch to-go or
eat immediately!

YAMS HAVE BEEN CULTIVATED IN AFRICA AND ASIA SINCE 50,000 BC, AND ARE FULL OF THE **BENEFICIAL ANTIOXIDANT PIGMENTS** KNOWN AS **CAROTENOIDS** THAT RUN RAMPANT IN FALL VEGGIES. YAMS ARE LOWER ON THE GLYCEMIC INDEX THAN POTATOES OR SWEET POTATOES. FULL OF COMPLEX CARBOHYDRATES TO KEEP YOU GOING ALL DAY LONG, YAMS ARE ALSO HIGH IN **POTASSIUM** -- A MINERAL WHICH HELPS REGULATE BLOOD PRESSURE AMONG OTHER THINGS -- AS WELL AS **MANGANESE**, A "BEAUTIFYING" MINERAL WHICH ASSISTS THE BODY IN CARBOHYDRATE METABOLISM AND IRON REGULATION.[78,79] YAMS ALSO HAVE A HISTORY OF AIDING KIDNEY FUNCTION, THE FEMALE ENDOCRINE SYSTEM, SYMPTOMS OF **PMS**, AND MENOPAUSE.[80]

COCONUT YAMFRIES
& HARVEST GREENS

1/2 yam, peeled & cubed
1 red potato, cubed
10 green beans, stemmed
1/3 c. red onion, diced
1 T. coconut oil
1 T. green onion, sliced
1/2 T. parsley, minced
1/2 T. cilantro, minced
1/4 t. turmeric
1/2 t. smoked sea salt
1/4 t. black pepper
1 pinch chipotle powder

Boil the yam and potato till tender,
and toss in the green beans for 1 min.
to blanch. <u>Set the green beans and 1/4
c. of the potatoes aside for tomorrow's
lunch.</u>

Brown the onions with the coconut
oil and then add the yam, potato and
spices, stirring to mix. To finish, turn
off the heat and stir in the fresh
herbs and green onions. Serve over this
tossed salad:

1 c. kale, minced
2/3 c. mixed baby greens
1/4 c. collard, minced
1/4 c. chard, minced
1/2 Persian cucumber, sliced long
1/3 carrot, peeled as shown
3 T. Ginger Flax Dressing (p.22)
1/8 t. curry or turmeric
1/8 t. garam masala
1 dash of cumin
1 pinch each of clove & paprika
1 t. Crystal Manna Flakes

Toss all the greens with the dressing,
spices and algae. Garnish with the Coconut
Yamfries, cucumber, peeled carrots and:

2 T. coconut flakes

Yummy yummy!

KALE CONTAINS COPIOUS AMOUNTS OF VITAMIN K, CHLOROPHYLL, AMINO ACIDS, AND (LIKE ALL BRASSICAS) ABOUT 10-15 SPECIAL SULPHUR PHYTONUTRIENTS, CALLED GLUCOSINOLATES, WHICH HAVE EXHIBITED INTENSE ANTI-CANCER PROPERTIES, EFFECTIVE AGAINST A VARIETY OF DIFFERENT CANCERS, BUT MOST NOTABLY THOSE FOUND IN THE LUNGS AND ALIMENTARY CANAL.[81] THOUGH STILL NOT FULLY UNDERSTOOD, THESE GLUCOSINOLATES APPEAR TO ACTIVATE DETOXIFYING ENZYMES WITHIN THE LIVER, WHICH CAN STOP POTENTIAL CARCINOGENS IN THEIR TRACKS. WHEN KALE IS CUT OR CHEWED, A PARTICULAR GLUCOSINOLATE COMPOUND CALLED SULPHORAPHANE IS ACTIVATED. SULPHORAPHANE IS EPIGENETIC, WHICH MEANS IT FAVORABLY INTERACTS WITH CELLULAR DNA, AND CAN BEHAVE AS A "SIGNAL" TELLING THE GENES TO SWITCH ON THEIR DEFENCES,[82] OFTEN BY INDUCING CANCER CELLS TO COMMIT SUICIDE![83]

starches and starchy proteins

Acorn Squash
Artichokes
Banana Squash
Beans
Beets
Bread
Carrot
Cereal
Corn
Grains
Lentils
Oats
Peanuts
Peas
Parsnips
Potatoes
Pumpkin
Quinoa
Rice
Rutabaga
Water Chestnuts
Yams
Young Coconut

EXCELLENT

fats

Olives
Avocado
Butter
Coconut
Oils

GOOD

EXCELLENT

Eat them __ALONE__ or leave them alone!

MELONS

7

vegetables

Asparagus
Beet Greens
Burdock
Broccoli
Brussels Sprouts
Cabbage
Cauliflower
Celery
Chard
Chicory
Collard Greens
Dandelions
Cucumber
Eggplant
Endive
Escarole
Garlic
Green Beans
Herbs
Kale
Kohlrabi Leeks
Lettuce
Mushrooms
Mustard Greens
Okra
Onions
Peppers
Radishes
Scallions
Spinach
Sprouts
Squash
Turnips
Watercress
Zucchini

Lettuce greens, sprouts, cucumber & celery combine favorably with fruits!

EXCELLENT

proteins

Nuts
Seeds
Eggs
Meats
Cheeses

__DRINK MILK ALONE!__

FAIR

Thank Thyme it's Friday!

acid fruits

Blackberry
Cranberry
Grapefruit
Lemon
Lime
Orange
Kumquat
Pomelo
Raspberry
Sour Apples
Sour Cherries
Sour Plums
Strawberry
Tangerines
Tomatoes

sweet fruits

Bananas
Dates
Dried Fruit
Figs
Grapes
Persimmons
Prunes
Sapote

GOOD

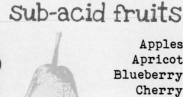

sub-acid fruits

Apples
Apricot
Blueberry
Cherry
Kiwi
Mango
Papaya
Peach
Pear
Plum

GOOD

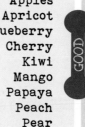

FOR DIGESTIVE STRENGTH, THE *BARBELLS* INDICATE WHICH FOOD GROUPINGS COMBINE WELL TOGETHER. EAT FRUITS 30–60 MINUTES BEFORE A MEAL, OR BY THEMSELVES. DESSERTS SHOULD ALWAYS BE EATEN ALONE AS A MEAL UNTO THEMSELVES. DRINK WATER 15 MINUTES BEFORE MEALS, OR 4 HOURS AFTERWARDS!

Can you stomach it?

Long debated, FOOD COMBINING is the polemic practice of eating foods in combinations that digest in a complimentary fashion, so as to maximize their nutrition and avoid internal putrefaction, bellyaches and bloating.[84] Food combining is sometimes referred to as TROPHOLOGY, also known as "the science of nutrition," or "alimentology."[85] Various health practitioners have long claimed there is no scientific evidence to support food combining, citing that our bodies produce a veritable "car wash" of enzymes to digest any combination of foods eaten together all at once, and claiming that it's pointless to differentiate the consumption of proteins and carbohydrates (or anything else for that matter), since most foods are comprised of proteins, carbohydrates, sugars and what have you.[86,87] However, the basic laws of chemistry, numerous studies (Pavlov, anyone?) and countless testimonials all suggest a direct connection between various foods and the different digestive juices secreted in response to them. According to Dr. Herbert Shelton, one of the founding fathers of food combining, it is a subject area "physiologists usually gloss over," despite the fact that they all agree "the character of the digestive juice secreted corresponds with the character of the food to be digested and that each food calls for its own specific modification of the digestive juice"[88,89] At the end of the day, the proof is in the figgy pudding. If you doubt whether or not your digestion can be affected by how you combine your foods, compare how you feel after eating a spoonful of everything in your fridge to eating a piece of fruit all by itself… the thought alone should offer you some evidence!

While it is true that all foods contain some percentage of carbohydrates, proteins, fats and sugars, which get treated to various acid and enzyme baths while grooving through the alimentary canal; proponents of food combining suggest that identifying the *prevailing nutritional compound* present in any given food (protein, carbohydrate, acid, sugar), and aligning its alchemical digestive requirements with other complimentary foods (if any) will alleviate alchemical contradictions -- also known as cramps and smelly situations.[90,91] For example, CARBOHYDRATES & PROTEINS SHOULD NOT BE EATEN TOGETHER because the alkaline loving amylase pytalin enzymes your mouth secretes to break down a starchy biscuit are neutralized by the strong gastric acid your stomach demands for splitting protein chains as soon as it detects the presence of a turkey drumstick.[92,93] Once their digestion has been retarded, overly acidified carbohydrates ferment prematurely in the low pH of potent gastric acid, while simultaneously compromising its potency and thus suspending or prolonging the timing and effectiveness of the entire digestive process.[94,95] Such digestive imbalances can cause significant problems in sensitive individuals, and frankly can give anyone a bad case of gas. While it's not uncommon for a certified nutritionist to argue that the stomach is by nature an acidic environment, and that starch digestion will always be inhibited there -- regardless of whether or not a protein is consumed, according to Dennis Nelson, author of *Maximizing Your Nutrition*, it has in fact been observed on numerous occasions throughout medical history that the pH of "gastric juice is variable, ranging from highly acidic to a mild acid or nearly neutral medium, depending on the type of food eaten."[96] Thus it would stand to reason that some improvement in digestion could be made by abstaining from eating a protein with your baked potato, so as to not signal for more acid in your stomach while you're already having a carbohydrate (or vice versa). In fact, individuals with sensitive plumbing (Crohn's, IBS, Colitis, allergies, etc.) find their symptoms all but disappear when they adhere to the guidelines set forth in food combining. As David Klein, Ph.D. personally observed, "within 24 hours of adopting a vegan diet and applying food combining, my g.i. system, which had been a virtual erupting volcano when I suffered with ulcerative colitis, completely quieted down."[97]

If the enzymatic alchemy argument doesn't jive with you, think of it this way: foods have different transit rates at which they move through your belly.[98] Melons are digested in about 30 minutes, while other fruits take 30-60 minutes to clear the stomach. After fruits, the gastric transit of greens, sprouts and veggies takes about an hour, followed by starchy veggies and grain, which take 1-2 hours to digest. Vegetarian proteins transit in 2-3 hours, while animal proteins don't leave the stomach for a minimum of 3-4 hours (8 hours or more for shellfish)![99] Considering these timetables, doesn't it seem natural that conflict could easily arise if you were to eat something that digests very quickly with something that digests very slowly? The extent to which someone is sensitive to the realities of food combining varies, so test it out and see how it works for you!

THE BLUEBERRY HAWAIIAN

1 c. wild blueberries, frozen
1 c. apple juice, unpasteurized
1/2 avocado
1/2 c. Persian cucumber, chopped
1/4 c. celery
1 small handful of mixed greens
3 T. ginger, peeled and chopped
1 lime, peeled
2 t. raw honey
1 T. flaxseed oil
6 drops orange essential oil (optional)
2/3 c. water
1/2 c. ice

SUPERCHARGE WITH SUPERFOODS:
1 t. bee pollen
1 t. Billy's Infinity C
1 t. Mineral Manna
1 t. pomegranate powder
1/2 t. (or more) E3Live, Billy's Infinity
Greens, or Spirulina Manna

Blend everything on high till smooth
and serve with a wedge of lime, or split
in two pint jars to drink throughout
the morning. Aloha!

BLUEBERRIES CONTAIN ANTHOCYANINS, A *PHENOLIC FLAVINOID* WHICH AFFECTS THE TASTE AND COLOR OF THE BERRY AND ALSO ACTS AS AN ANTIOXIDANT. DURING THE GROWTH PHASE OF THE BLUEBERRY SHRUB, SUNLIGHT AFFECTS THE CONCENTRATION OF PHENOLICS IN THE BERRY'S SKIN. REMEMBER, ANTIOXIDANTS ARE MOLECULES WHICH ACTUALLY SLOW OR PREVENT THE OXIDATION OF OTHER MOLECULES. IN THE HUMAN BODY, MOLECULAR OXIDATION PRODUCES FREE-RADICALS, WHICH STEAL ELECTRONS FROM THE MOLECULES OF HEALTHY CELLS, DAMAGING THEM AND SETTING OFF CHAIN REACTIONS BY TURNING THEM INTO FREE-RADICALS THEMSELVES. THIS PROCESS IS REFERRED TO AS "OXIDATIVE STRESS" AND IS A COMPONENT IN AGING AND MANY DIFFERENT TYPES OF DISEASES.[100] TO COMBAT OXIDATIVE STRESS, THE BODY LIKES TO KEEP HANDY A PLETHORA OF DIFFERENT ANTIOXIDANTS. IN ADDITION TO FRUIT AND VEGETABLE PIGMENTS LIKE CAROTENOIDS AND ANTHOCYANINS, SOME OF THESE ANTIOXIDANTS INCLUDE ENZYMES LIKE SUPEROXIDE DISMUTASE, CATALASE, AND PEROXIDASE, AS WELL AS VITAMIN C, VITAMIN E, AND GLUTATHIONE.[101] ANTIOXIDANT CONTENT IN FOODS ARE MEASURED USING A PROCESS WHICH TESTS THE *OXYGEN RADICAL ABSORPTION CAPACITY (ORAC)*. BLUEBERRIES HAVE ONE OF THE HIGHER KNOWN ORAC VALUES, WHILE *RAW CACAO* HAS THE HIGHEST.[102]

BASTARD NICOISE SALAD

2-3 c. romaine lettuce & watercress, chopped
1 Persian cucumber, sliced
2 okras, sliced thin
1/2 small tomato, cubed
2 radishes, sliced
1/2 avocado, sliced
1 small shallot, sliced
10 oil cured black olives, pitted
1 T. parsley, minced
10 green beans, blanched (p.54)
1/4 c. boiled potatoes, cubed (p.54)

Toss the romaine lettuce and watercress together with the following:

1/4 c. Black Olive Dressing
1 t. balsamic vinegar
1 clove garlic, minced
1/2 t. whole grain mustard
1/4 t. nutritional yeast
1/4 t. black pepper
1/4 t. rubbed sage
1/4 t. rosemary
1/4 t. thyme
1/4 t. pink Himalayan salt

Arrange dressed greens in a bowl. Place the salad veggies along with the green beans and boiled potatoes from last night on top in cute little bunches. Garnish with parsley and sprouts if you got 'em!

ROMAINE LETTUCE ALONG WITH CUCUMBERS, RADISHES, OLIVES, ONION, OKRA, AVOCADOS AND TOMATOES, ALL HAVE AMAZING MINERAL PROPERTIES THAT BEAUTIFY YOU FROM THE INSIDE OUT. THE MAGNESIUM, SULPHUR, SILICON, HEALTHY FATS AND FAT SOLUBLE LYCOPENE IN THESE FOODS FEED YOUR HAIR, SKIN AND NAILS AT A CELLULAR LEVEL.[103] AN UPDATE ON AN OLD CLASSIC, THE DRESSING FOR THIS SALAD IS ALSO A TASTY LITTLE ANTI-COLD & FLU REMEDY! GARLIC, LEMON, PARSLEY, SAGE, ROSEMARY AND THYME ALL HAVE POWERFUL IMMUNE BOOSTING PROPERTIES.[104] BOOST THE DRESSING'S THERAPEUTIC PROPERTIES BY SWAPPING OUT THE BALSAMIC WITH RAW APPLE CIDER VINEGAR TO REGULATE BLOOD PRESSURE, BALANCE YOUR CHOLESTEROL, AND SUPPORT YOUR LIVER AND GALLBLADDER WITH BREAKING DOWN FATS.[105]

PRETTY ME UP SALAD

1 c. mixed baby greens
1/2 c. kale, minced
1/3 c. chard, minced
1/4 c. celery, sliced thin
1 radish, julienned
2" burdock root, julienned
2" carrot, julienned
1/4 c. Persian cucumber, sliced
1/4 avocado, sliced
2 T. pickled ginger, chopped
1 T. green onion, sliced
1 T. parsley, minced
9 macadamia nuts, chopped
9 black olives, pitted & chopped

Mix the kale, chard, and mixed baby greens together in a large bowl. Sprinkle with the remaining veggies, herbs, nuts, olives and pickled ginger. Serve with:

3 T. Ginger Flax Dressing (p.22)

Garnish with sprouts!

SULPHUR-IRON-SILICON-MANGANESE-ZINC

SHOULD BE A MODERN DAY MANTRA FOR EVERYONE WHO WANTS TO FEEL AND LOOK BETTER. THE QUALITIES THAT MAKE SOMEONE VITAL, ATTRACTIVE AND MAGNETIC STEM FROM THE PRESENCE OF THESE MINERALS IN THEIR TISSUES.[106] SULPHUR TRANSFORMS THE CROSS LINKAGES OF SCAR TISSUE AND STRENGTHENS THE STRUCTURE OF CONNECTIVE TISSUES IN MUSCLES AND JOINTS. IRON, STORED IN THE HEMOGLOBIN OF YOUR BLOOD, CARRIES OXYGEN TO ALL YOUR TISSUES. SILICON IS USED PRIMARILY BY CONNECTIVE TISSUES LIKE COLLAGEN AND ELASTIN, WITH THE LARGEST QUANTITIES OF IT FOUND IN YOUR HAIR AND NAILS. MANGANESE SUPPORTS THE FORMATION OF CARTILAGE AND THE OXYGENATION OF BRAIN AND NERVE CELLS. ZINC PROMOTES CELL DIVISION, REPAIR & GROWTH, AND IS DISBURSED THROUGH THE LYMPHATIC SYSTEM TO ASSIST WITH WASTE ELIMINATION, OXYGENATION, AND TISSUE REPAIR. THE BODY USES ZINC TO STRENGTHEN HAIR FOLLICLES, EYESIGHT, THE PROSTATE, AND TO MAINTAIN ITS COLLAGEN SUPPLY.[107] ALL OF THESE MINERALS ARE FOUND IN ABUNDANCE IN THIS SALAD, SO EAT UP AND LOVE YOUR GORGEOUS SELF!!!

Saturday Morning Cartoons

In his seminal work *The China Study*, Dr. T. Colin Campbell, professor emeritus of Cornell University, concludes that animal products like meat, dairy and eggs contribute to the proliferation of cancer cells in the body, while a vegan diet of antioxidant rich fruits and vegetables is protective against cancer, as well as a number of other diseases. Dr. Campbell's research is especially significant if you consider the fact that he grew up on a dairy farm and originally set out to prove the nutritional importance of animal protein in the human diet.[108] Far from ending the debate about human diets, it's prompted a lively discussion. As far as evolution goes, we're the new kids on the block, and despite arguments that human beings are really like rats or bears or pigs, our closest genetic relative is the Bonobo, *Pan paniscus*, also known at one time as the "pygmy chimpanzee."[109] Bonobos PRIMARILY eat fruits, vegetables, leaves, nuts/seeds & insects, but OCCASIONALLY they'll hunt and eat other small mammals -- usually little monkeys.[110] Clearly, human beings are behaviorally omnivorous, but many seem quick to forget that we are the most genetically and physiologically similar to the aforementioned tropical forager, who instinctively consumes a predominantly vegetarian diet. In comparing the anatomical and physiological features of herbivores, carnivores and omnivores (the latter two being nearly identical), Dr. Milton R. Mills concludes that human beings are in fact "committed" herbivores by design.[111] Here's why:

1) Like other herbivorous creatures, our tongue has the capacity to detect starches and trigger the release of PTYALIN into the alkaline medium of our saliva, which begins digesting starches while we chew. Carnivores have acidic saliva, cannot produce any ptyalin whatsoever, and feed by swallowing meat whole and unchewed.[112] 2) Vegetable matter contains large amounts of "indigestible fibers," and so, like other hindgut fermenting herbivores who eat mostly soft vegetation, we are equipped with a lengthy puckered, small intestinal tract to digest it. Our 22-30 foot intestinal maze allows for the slow proliferation and absorption of nutrients, as cultivated through the enzymatic bacterial fermentation of plant matter. In contrast, carnivore intestines are short and smooth for rapid processing to avoid the putrefaction of flesh foods.[113] 3) Our faces are flat, we have no claws, and our tongue, facial musculature and jaws permit side to side chewing on the flat surfaces of our molar teeth. Your canines? They're actually the dullest of all the primates who have largely been classified as frugivores (save for the occasional monkey snack). By comparison, carnivorous creatures have long snouts, sharp claws and a mouth full of spade shaped teeth. Coupled with the powerful temporalis muscle that controls their hinge jaw, carnivore teeth are capable of shearing flesh off bone.[114] 4) Viral cat videos aside, do YOU think kittens and other small furry creatures are cute? Or, does the idea of attacking and killing a small rodent, mammal, or bird, thrill you to the point of salivation? If you're not convinced of your inherent "vegetarianism," you might jive with the "Raw Paleo Diet," which advocates (contrary to popular medical opinion) that animal products are best consumed RAW (enzymatically active) and as fresh as possible -- the way carnivores and "other omnivores" eat them. Sashimi, anyone? Ceviché? Steak tartare?

In 1832, Charles Darwin famously observed finches on the Galapagos Islands with different beak sizes that seemed to correlate with their environmental and dietary options.[115] These musings laid the groundwork for Darwin's *The Origin of Species*, which popularized his theories about evolution and natural selection. Today we've confirmed all 13 species of "Darwin's finches" originated from a single species of finch on the mainland of South America, in a classic example of *adaptive radiation*.[116] Recently, biologists Peter and Rosemary Grant confirmed such evolution "in action."[117] When faced with competition from larger finches with a bigger beak for cracking large seeds, the medium ground finches, *Geospiza fortis*, survived by using their small beaks to forage for little seeds instead. The trait of the smaller beak, as well as the dietary willingness for smaller seeds, enabled these birds to thrive and reproduce during a food scarcity, which further diminished their beak size within just a few generations.[118] Information like this is exciting because it underscores how we become what we eat. So my own position is this: no species is ever finished. At the end of the day there isn't a "right" or "wrong" diet. Genotypical variability for adaptation exists within all of us, so we are all works in progress! If you don't contain the subtle genetic variations required to thrive on your chosen diet and environmental pressures, your body may express maladaptations such as allergies and disease. That being said, I think we can all hedge our bets a bit by providing our physiology with as much of the food it currently appears to be most adapted to digest.

CRAN-RAZZ COCONUT PARFAIT

3/4 c. young coconut meat
1/2 c. young coconut water or Nut Mylk (p.20)
6 macadamia nuts, soaked
1/4 lime, peeled
2 t. coconut oil
1 t. raw honey
1/4 t. ground vanilla bean

If you're looking for the best way to open a coconut, go for
the cleaver. However, if you don't have a cleaver, poke the flat
bottom of the coconut with a paring knife until you pierce the
"soft eye," and drain out the water. Like a wild primate, bang
the empty coconut on the ground until it breaks and scoop out
the meat. Next, blend the macadamias with 1/4 c. coconut water
until smooth, and then add in the remaining ingredients above
and blend everything together into a thick cream. Pour into a
glass and plop in 12 FRESH OR DEFROSTED RASPBERRIES. Without
washing the blender, puree the following:

2/3 c. raspberries, frozen
1/4 c. cranberries
1 T. flaxseed oil
2 t. goji berries
2 t. raw honey
2/3 c. water
1/2 c. ice

SUPPLEMENT SUPER-BOOSTER:
2 t. pomegranate powder
1 t. bee pollen
1 t. Billy's Infinity C

Pour over the berries and coconut cream and enjoy!

LYCOPENE

AS YOU MAY RECALL, IS ANOTHER FRIENDLY NEIGHBORHOOD CAROTENOID WITH ANTIOXIDANT PROPERTIES. THOUGH MOSTLY USED BY RED BLOOD CELLS AND REPRODUCTIVE ORGANS, LYCOPENE ALSO SUPPORTS CARDIOVASCULAR HEALTH.[119] LUCKY FOR YOU, LYCOPENE IS READILY AVAILABLE IN THE RED-PIGMENTED INGREDIENTS OF THIS SMOOTHIE! A FAT SOLUBLE PHYTOCHEMICAL, LYCOPENE IS BEST ABSORBED BY THE DIGESTIVE SYSTEM IN THE PRESENCE OF DIETARY FATS. FORTUNATELY, THE HEART HEALTHY FATS SUPPLIED BY THE MACADAMIA NUTS, COCONUT AND FLAXSEED OIL IN THIS SMOOTHIE NOT ONLY PROVIDE AN EXCELLENT FATTY MEDIUM FOR LYCOPENE ABSORPTION, BUT THEY ALSO SUPPORT THE PRODUCTION OF HDL (THE GOOD CHOLESTEROL THAT HELPS SWEEP THE BAD "LDL" CHOLESTEROL OUT OF YOUR VEINS). WHILE COCONUT OIL IS A NATURALLY SATURATED FAT, IT'S ALSO MOSTLY COMPRISED OF MEDIUM CHAIN FATTY ACIDS, WHICH REQUIRE VIRTUALLY NO EFFORT ON THE PART OF THE BODY TO METABOLIZE AND STORE. IN FACT, MANY STUDIES HAVE INDICATED THAT COCONUT CONSUMPTION CAN ACTUALLY LOWER LDL, BOOST HDL AND PROVIDE OTHER HEART PROTECTIVE QUALITIES AS WELL.[120,121] AND WHAT DO YOU KNOW? THE COUNTRIES WITH THE HIGHEST PALM & COCONUT FAT CONSUMPTION ALSO HAVE THE LOWEST INCIDENCES OF HEART DISEASE.[122]

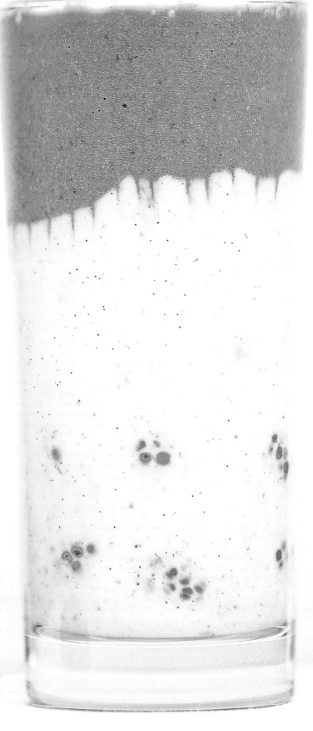

GUACATACOS

1/2 c avocado, cubed
2 T. tomato, diced
1 1/2 T. red onion, minced
1 1/2 T. celery, diced
1 T. corn kernels, off the cob
1 T. cilantro, minced
1 T. lime juice
1 T. Ginger Flax Dressing (p.22)
1 small clove garlic, minced
1 t. jalapeno, minced

1/4 t. sea salt & 1 pinch black pepper
1 pinch chipotle & a dash of cumin!

Gently mix the above ingredients in a bowl.
Gently toast 2-3 sprouted corn tortillas,
scoop in the guacamole, and top with:

2/3 c. mixed baby greens or romaine, minced
2 T. golden beet, shredded
2 T. Live Zing or Wild Brine sauerkraut
2 T. Country Fair S'nutty (p.20)
2 T. Black Olive Dressing (p.22)

FERMENTATION IS THE BIOCHEMICAL PROCESS BY WHICH ORGANIC MATTER "DIGESTS" ITSELF. ANAEROBIC FERMENTATION BEGINS WHEN CELLS ARE DEPRIVED OF OXYGEN AND BEGIN EMITTING LACTIC ACID AS A BYPRODUCT OF THEIR ATTEMPT TO "BREATHE WITHOUT AIR." THIS INVITES PARTICIPATION FROM "LACTIC ACID BACTERIA" (FOUND EVERYWHERE IN TRACE AMOUNTS), WHO SET UP CAMP AND CULTURE THE FOOD, FEEDING OFF THE LACTIC ACID PRODUCED BY DROWNING CELLS. THE NUTRITIONAL PROFILE OF CULTURED, FERMENTED FOODS "BLOOMS" WITH BIOAVAILABLE PROTEINS, VITAMINS AND AMINO ACIDS, AS LAB UNLOCK NUTRITION IN PLANT FIBER AND EMIT NUTRITIONAL BY-PRODUCTS LIKE VITAMIN B AND K ALONG THE WAY.[123] FERMENTED FOODS ARE THE "ORIGINAL" PROBIOTICS, AND OFFER A NATURAL, TIME TESTED MEANS OF RE-SEEDING THE BENEFICIAL FLORA LIVING IN THE MAZE OF YOUR INTESTINES.[124,125] A HEALTHY RESERVOIR OF PROBIOTICS IS INTEGRAL TO THE BODY'S IMMUNE SYSTEM, OFFERING PROTECTION AGAINST A NUMBER OF VIRAL, BACTERIAL, AND OTHER AILMENTS. FOR EXAMPLE, LAB INHIBIT THE ACTIVITY OF CERTAIN ENZYMES THAT MIGHT OTHERWISE CONTRIBUTE TO COLON CANCER.[126]

SEA MONSTER SALAD

1/8 c. hijiki, dry
1/8 c. arame, dry
1/3 c carrot, julienned
1/3 c. summer squash, julienned
1 T. green onion, sliced
1 T. lemon juice
1 T. raw coconut nectar
1 T. nama shoyu
1 1/2 t. ginger, grated
1 t. umeboshi plum vinegar
1 t. flaxseed oil
1 t. sesame seeds
1/2 t. toasted sesame oil

Soak the seaweeds for about 10 minutes.
Drain the water and toss the seaweed with
the ingredients listed above.

Serve with:

1/2 avocado, sliced
4 handfuls mixed baby greens
10 long sprouts (optional)
2-3 T. Miso Much Love Tahini Dressing (p.22)
2-3 T. Live Zing or Wild Brine sauerkraut

CONGRATULATIONS!

You made it through the week!

*P.S. The Sea Monster Salad works great as
a taco filling, too!*

SESAME SEEDS POSSES THE BENEFICIAL FIBERS SESAMIN AND SESAMOLIN, TWO LIGNANS THAT EXHIBIT A CHOLESTEROL LOWERING EFFECT ON THE BODY. SESAME SEEDS ALSO POSSES THE HIGHEST NUMBER OF PHYTOSTEROLS OF ANY NUT OR SEED. PHYTOSTEROLS ARE COMPOUNDS WHOSE CHEMICAL STRUCTURE RESEMBLES THAT OF CHOLESTEROL. IF EATEN IN REGULAR QUANTITIES, PHYTOSTEROLS CAN LOWER CHOLESTEROL LEVELS IN THE BLOOD, BOOST THE IMMUNE SYSTEM, AND PREVENT AGAINST CERTAIN CANCERS.[127] THE HIGH COPPER CONTENT OF SESAME SUPPORTS CROSS-LINKAGES IN COLLAGEN AND ELASTIN FORMATION, AS WELL AS ANTI-INFLAMMATORY ENZYME SYSTEMS. THE FATS IN SESAME SEEDS COMBINED WITH THE SODIUM AND POTASSIUM OF THE SEAWEEDS MAKE AN EXCELLENT PAIRING WITH SULPHUR RICH FOODS LIKE FERMENTED CABBAGE, SINCE THEY COUNTERACT THE "HEATING" EFFECT SULPHUR HAS IN THE GUT.[128] DESPITE THE GASEOUS DISCOMFORTS SULPHUR RICH FOODS CAN CREATE, THEY'RE SUPER CRITICAL TO INCLUDE IN THE DIET SINCE IT'S VERY EASY TO BECOME DEFICIENT IN THIS VITAL MINERAL. EATEN ALONE, HIGH POTASSIUM/SODIUM FOODS TEND TO PUMP THE BODY'S SULPHUR RESERVES DRY. AMAZINGLY, SULPHUR RICH FOODS ALL SEEM TO HAVE PROFOUND ANTI-CANCER PROPERTIES, WHICH COULD SUGGEST A LINK BETWEEN CANCER AND A SULPHUR DEFICIENCY.[129]

YOGA FEELS SO GOOD.

9

In Circulation

BIKING FEELS SO GOOD!

JUMPING...!

...FEELS...!

...SO GOOD...!

...HIKING *HUFF* FEELS SO GOOD!

Enter the bloodstream

THE BEST GASOLINE in the world won't get you very far if you haven't got a working fuel pump to circulate it through your engine. In the human body, that part is the heart. If your heart rate isn't up, how is your body supposed to move all the good stuff you've put down your gullet into your bloodstream to feed your outermost reaches of cellular tissue? Everything we've discussed up until this point has been about the processes by which chewing, acids, enzymes, and probiotic fermentation digests foodstuffs into chemical structures small enough to be filtered into your bloodstream through your porous intestinal walls; and then distributed throughout your tissues to be absorbed through the membranes of your cells and converted into energy. In other words -- the process by which your body converts whole foods into little bites small enough to feed your hungry cells. Essentially, the human body is like an elaborate juicer/composting machine; but it comes with a HAND CRANK MOTOR and the efficiency of our metabolic performance is greatly determined by how fast we turn the crank. Yes, I'm talking about booty shakin', people!

EXERCISE IS THE MAGIC INGREDIENT. You can have a fantastic diet and never be truly healthy if all of your perfect nutrition isn't absorbed and circulated through your system. We are all bodies in motion designed to move, stretch and bend in every which way. Whether it's hiking, yoga, dance, jogging, biking, weight training, sports, dog walking, yard work, or simply playing in the woods, physical activity is essential to health and the prevention of disease. In 2001, the American Cancer Prevention Society established new guidelines, declaring exercise to be just as important as a balanced diet when it comes to cancer prevention. According to Abby Bloch, chairwoman of the advisory panel who created the guidelines, regular exercise "is a primary component of preventing cancer."[130] In fact, Georgetown Lombardi Comprehensive Cancer Center recently announced findings that "rigorous" aerobic exercise for a mere two hours a week can reduce the risk of breast cancer by as much as 64%.[131] Moreover, the more we move, the more we keep moving ALL THROUGH OUR LIVES.[132] The benefits of movement include looking, feeling and sleeping better, a reduction in all manners of chronic illnesses, a spark in self-confidence, increased cardiovascular health, and the ability to be more fully ourselves and experience the world with joy. So move it or lose it, folks!

As children we move all the time - running, jumping, skipping. We delight in the physical expression of the human form, eager to experience new movements and discover our physical limits. Heck, the physical sensations associated with bodily movements of all kinds are the bedrock of the human experience! But even if you hate exercise, you can mentally retrain yourself to love the "burn." The next time you're feeling uncomfortable, just repeat in your mind "running feels so good!" or "stretching feels so good!" or "hiking feels so good!" Before you know it, you'll be a believer!

It's never too late to begin moving or eating better. Oftentimes it's only once we start that we realize just how poorly we've been feeling! The sense of wellbeing that exercise engenders is instantaneous, and can perpetuate a certain craving for more. Exercise releases ENDORPHINS, euphoric "feel good" chemicals that reduce our perception of pain, boost immunity and cardiovascular health, and "trigger a positive feeling in the body, similar to that of morphine."[133] These feelings of wellbeing translate into a viable, effective, and underutilized treatment for depression, which, according to Harvard Health Publications, can have longer lasting effects than antidepressants.[134,135] So seize every opportunity you can: a dance class at your local community college, a Saturday hike with a friend, pilates, a run around the block, a bike ride to the grocery store, taking the stairs, pole dancing, tennis, jumping up and down for 10 minutes, even dancing around your apartment in your underwear... ANYTHING! Remember, beginnings, however humble, are still beginnings. Everything in nature begins with a singular impulse. From the tiniest germ of being, life manifests outward into the universe. Wherever you may be in your journey, you can always take the first step towards reinvention.

...MMMM...

...THIS TASTES AMAZING!

I'VE FELT INCREDIBLE ALL WEEK.

I CAN'T BELIEVE I'M ALMOST DONE. NOTHING BUT A BUNCH OF LISTS LEFT.

THAT'S RIGHT, BUT THESE LAST FEW PAGES MAY BE THE **BEST OF ALL**, AS THEY CONTAIN A LIST OF SEASONAL INGREDIENTS AND A **SUPERFOOD APPENDIX**, PACKED WITH NUTRITIONAL INFORMATION ABOUT THE INGREDIENTS IN THIS BOOK!!

The end of the book prompted a rather relevant evaluation of her very existence.... among other things.

WHAT'S GONNA HAPPEN TO ME WHEN I FINISH THE BOOK?

WILL I GO BACK TO MY OLD WAYS?

OR WILL I JUST DISAPPEAR?

WILL THAT CUTE GUY FROM THE COFFEE SHOP EVER CALL?!? MAYBE I SHOULD SKIP AHEAD...

PHEW... THAT'S A RELIEF!

SEASONAL FALL FOODS:

WOW! A LIST OF SEASONAL FOODS, HOW HELPFUL! SO I COULD SWAP OUT SOME OF THE INGREDIENTS WITH THE STUFF ON THESE LISTS IF I FELT... INSPIRED?

Acorn Squash	Herbs
Apples	Horseradish
Artichokes	Jerusalem Artichokes
Arugula	Kale
Beets	Kohlrabi
Belgian Endive	Leeks
Bell Peppers	Lemongrass
Broccoli/Broccolini	Lettuces/Greens
Brussels sprouts	Limes
Butternut Squash	Mushrooms
Cabbage	Okra
Carrots	Onions
Cauliflower	Parsnips
Celeriac/celery root	Pears
Celery	Persimmons
Chard	Pomegranates
Chicories	Potatoes
Chiles	Pumpkins
Cranberries	Quinces
Edamame	Radicchio
Eggplant	Radishes
Escarole	Rutabagas
Fennel	Shallots
Figs	Sweet potatoes
Frisée	Tomatillos
Garlic	Turnips
Grapes	Winter Squash
Green Beans	Yams
Green Onions	Zucchini

YES!! THIS BOOK IS A TOOL TO BE INTEGRATED INTO YOUR LIFE. PLAY AND EXPERIMENT WITH WHAT YOU'VE LEARNED AND PUT TOGETHER CREATIVE NEW MEALS... EXPERIMENT WITH THE LEFTOVERS!

UM... I DON'T KNOW THAT I'M THERE YET... MAYBE NEXT WEEK?

BABY STEPS ARE OK, TOO.

THE IMPORTANT THING TO REMEMBER IS THAT THE WAY YOU FEEL DIRECTLY AFFECTS THE WAY YOU PERCEIVE THE WORLD AROUND YOU!! MAKE THE WORLD WONDERFUL JUST BY TAKING CARE OF YOURSELF.

RIING!!!

RRIING!

GASP... WHO COULD THAT BE...?

HELLO? OH HI THERE! WHAT A PLEASANT SURPRISE...!

...A HIKE AFTER LUNCH? THAT SOUNDS LOVELY!

WAIT A MINUTE, WHERE ARE YOU GOING? YOU HAVEN'T FINISHED YOUR TACOS! AND WE STILL NEED TO GO OVER THE SUPER NUTRITION APPENDIX ON PAGE 80...?!?

IN AN HOUR...?

THERE'S EVEN A BONUS CHOCOLATE RECIPE!!!

HOLD ON A SEC... CHOCOLATE?

THAT'S RIGHT! TAKE A SNEAK PEEK AT PAGE 78!

YUMMY!...UH, SORRY... JUST TALKING TO MY COMIC BOO... NEVERMIND.

I'M GONNA HANG UP NOW... I'LL SEE YOU SOON! OK, BYE!!!

NOW, WHERE IS THAT BACKPACK?

WATER BOTTLE, HAT, SWEATER... APPLE! IT FEELS GOOD TO BE GETTING OUT OF THE HOUSE!

HALLELUJAH!

YOU'RE EATING RIGHT AND GOING FOR A HIKE! LOOKS LIKE THE SUPER-SUBCONSCIOUS HAS VANQUISHED SELF-SABOTAGE YET AGAIN!

Away Ingrid went to meet her friend with the book in tow. Little did she know, the Super-Subconscious cannot be confined to a mere comic book. It travels within us all wherever we may go.

OH MY...

WHAT A GLORIOUS DAY!

LIFE BY CHOCOLATE

1 c. raw cacao butter
2/3 c. raw cacao powder
3 T. raw coconut sugar crystals
3 T. raw coconut nectar
1 T. coconut oil
1/2 t. maca
1/2 t. Billy's Infinity Greens
1/2 t. ground vanilla bean
1/4 t. lemon zest
1/4 t. pink salt

Heat 2 c. water on the stove until nice and steamy. Warm a mixing bowl by placing it over the steamy water. Mince the cacao butter into shavings to fill your measuring cup, and add it to the warm mixing bowl so it can melt, but prevent it from getting too hot by taking the mixing bowl off the pot once it gets going. Stir in the remaining ingredients, mix well (a food processor can be helpful). Pour into chocolate moulds or ice cube trays, freeze, and wrap in foil to store!

RAW CACAO WAS USED AS A CURRENCY IN ANCIENT TIMES, AND CHOCO- LATE LOVERS AROUND THE WORLD HAVE LONG UNDERSTOOD WHY. WITH ONE OF THE HIGHEST KNOWN ORAC VALUES OF ANY KNOWN FOOD (OVER 95,000 UNITS!), CACAO IS THE MOST PHARMACOLOGICALLY COMPLEX FOOD IN THE RAINFOREST, CONTAIN- ING CLOSE TO 1,200 DIFFERENT CHEMICAL COMPOUNDS![136] AS PREVIOUSLY DISCUSSED, TWO OF THOSE COMPOUNDS ARE PEA AND ANANDAMIDE, THE CHEMICALS IN YOUR BRAIN RESPONSIBLE FOR FEELINGS OF "LOVE" AND "BLISS." AS MIRANDA INGRAM ONCE SAID, "IT'S NOT THAT CHOCOLATES ARE A SUBSTITUTE FOR LOVE. LOVE IS A SUBSTITUTE FOR CHOCOLATE. CHOCOLATE IS, LET'S FACE IT, FAR MORE RELIABLE THAN A MAN..."

3.6 billion years ago, blue-green algae evolves on earth. It produces oxygen and becomes the base of the food chain for all life to come.

450 million years ago, the first plants creep onto the land.

418 million years ago, plants begin to bear seeds.

Plantlife on Earth

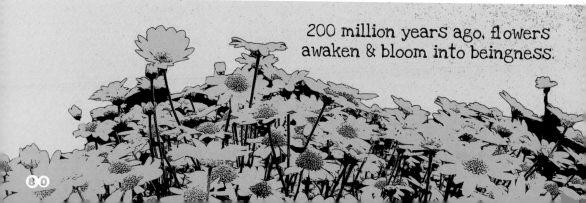

200 million years ago, flowers awaken & bloom into beingness.

SUPER NUTRITION APPENDIX

herein lie some fun facts about the nutritional content of many of the ingredients used in this issue! This information has largely been compiled from the referemnces cited in the endnotes on pages 90-94.

ACAI <u>Vitamins</u>: A, B1, B2, B3, C, E. <u>Minerals</u>: potassium, phosphorus, calcium, iron, copper, cobalt, chromium and manganese. <u>Compounds</u>: polyphenol antioxidant pigments like anthocyanins (thirty times the amount in red wine) and proanthocyanidins, and resveratrol. <u>Also contains</u>: Omega 3 and 6 essential fatty acids in a ratio that resembles olive oil, oleic acid, palmitic acid, and phytosterols like beta-sitosterol. <u>Properties</u>: anti-inflammatory, antimutagenic, anticancer, and antibacterial. Because of its resveratrol and unique spectrum of EFA's and antioxidant phytonutrients, Acai is considered one of the best foods for weightloss and rejuvenation.

APHANIZOMENON FLOS-AQUAE "E3LIVE" & "CRYSTAL MANNA" ALGAE <u>Vitamins</u>: A, B1, B2, B3, B5, B6, B9, B12, C, E, H, choline. <u>Minerals</u>: boron, calcium, chloride, chromium, cobalt, copper, fluoride, germanium, iodine, iron, magnesium, manganese, molybdenum, nickel, phosphorus, potassium, selenium, silicon, sodium, tin, titanium, vanadium, zinc. <u>Compounds</u>: phenylethylamine (PEA), polyphenol antioxidant pigments aphanin, alpha-carotene, beta-carotene, chlorophyll, cryptoxanthin, lycopene, lutein, and phycocyanin; the amino acids alanine, arginine, asparagine, aspartic acid, glutamine, glutamic acid, glycine, histidine, isoleucine, leucine, lysine, methionine, phenylalanine, proline, sarcosine, serine, tryptophan, tyrosine, and threonine, valine; and some unique immune stimulating polysaccharides. <u>Also Contains</u>: Omega 3 and 6 essential fatty acids. <u>Properties</u>: Nearly every ailment know to humankind sees some benefit from the inclusion of this incredible algae, as it supports the nervous, digestive, cardiovascular, and endocrine systems, promotes intestinal health, and balances blood sugar. AFA is a considered a prokaryote because is lacks a membrane-bound nucleus. Harvested from the organic, nutrient dense and sunlight fed waters of Klamath Lake, AFA is considered a "super" blue green algae, due to having more bioavailable chlorophyll than any other known food. Given that algae is basically the "mother" of all life on earth, it's not surprising that it's spiral appearance resembles the double helix of DNA, or that 97% of the nutrition in AFA is easily and almost immediately absorbed upon consumption. AFA has the unique property of enchancing the release of stem cells from bone marror and promoting their migration into tissues to faciliate healing and repair. Loaded with the "love chemical" PEA, AFA alleviates mood swings and boosts neurological functions as well -- making it effective as an overall mood and health enhancing, adaptogenic supplement. Despite some claims of toxicity, Drapeau reports in his book *Primordial Food*, "In Klamath Lake, nearly ten years of intense testing has failed to reveal the presence of any neurotoxins in its AFA. In 1998 the opinion among scientists was that AFA did not contain neurotoxins and that the original samples that had been identified as AFA were likely another species."

APPLE <u>Vitamins</u>: A, B3, B5, B6, B9, C, E, K, P, choline, and betaine. <u>Minerals</u>: magnesium, iron, calcium, sodium, phosphorus, potassium, and fluoride. <u>Compounds</u>: the polyphenol antioxidants like phloridzin and the flavinoid quercetin; the amino acids alanine, arginine, asparagine, aspartic acid, glutamic acid, glycine, histidine, isoleucine, leucine, lysine, methionine, phenylalanine, proline, serine, tryptophan, tyrosine, threonine, and valine; as well as acetic acid, malic acid, propionic acid, and lactic acid. <u>Also Contains</u>: Omega 3 and 6 essential fatty acids, phytosterols, and pectin. <u>Properties</u>: antioxidant, mild anti-inflammatory. The antioxidants and organic compounds in apples not only inhibit glycation (a major contributor to cellular aging), burn belly fat, boost energy and endurance, stabilize blood glucose, and lower fat overall in the bloodstream; but they also inhibit the formation of dental and arterial plaque.

APPLE CIDER VINEGAR (RAW) <u>Vitamins</u>: A, B1, B2, B6, C, E, and P. <u>Minerals</u>: magnesium, iron, calcium, sodium, sulfur, copper, phosphorus, silicon, chlorine, fluorine and potassium. <u>Compounds</u>: acetic acid, malic acid, propionic acid, lactic acid. <u>Also Contains</u>: amino acids and roughage in the form of potash and apple pectin. <u>Properties</u>: antifungal, antibacterial, and antiviral. Apple cider vinegar assists in metabolizing fats, flushing out toxins, and generally detoxifying the liver. You'll know your vinegar is alive if it contains long cultured, strands floating in it.

ALMONDS Vitamins: A, B1, B2, B3, B5, B6, B9, E, choline, betaine. Minerals: iron, potassium, phosphorus, magnesium, calcium, manganese, copper, sodium, selenium, zinc. Compounds: the amino acids alanine, arginine, asparagine, aspartic acid, glutamic acid, glycine, histidine, isoleucine, leucine, lysine, methionine, phenylalanine, proline, serine, tryptophan, tyrosine, threonine, and valine; Also Contains: Omega 3 and 6 essential fatty acids, as well as oleic and palmitoleic acids. Properties: antioxidant. Abundant in monounsaturated fats, almonds, like other raw nuts, have the ability to reduce LDL levels while boosting HDL levels in the bloodstream when consumed on a daily basis, lowering the risk of heart disease and atherosclerosis. Almonds are also rich in vitamin E, which provides the largest organ in the body -- your skin -- a defenses against free radicals; as well as magnesium, which helps regulate blood flow through the body.

ARAME Vitamin: A, B2. Minerals: iodine, calcium, iron, potassium, zinc and many other trace minerals. Compounds: mannitol (non-caloric sugar alcohol), polysaccharide laminarin and the tripeptide eisenin. Also Contains: alginate. Properties: anti-carcinogenic. A species of kelp, arame counteracts high blood pressure, promotes soft, wrinkle free skin, enhances hair sheen, prevents hair loss, AND has traditionally been used as a cure-all for the female reproductive organs. Remember, all your cells need the iodine found in sea veggies to stay healthy and function properly, and low iodine levels have been linked to breast cancer, thyroid issues, and a number of other ailments. Sea veggies interfere with estrogen synthesis in fat cells the same way chemotherapy does, which makes them a great addition to your dinner plate for both preventing and combating cancer!

AVOCADO Vitamins: A, B1, B2, B3, B5, B6, B9, C, E, K, choline, betaine. Minerals: calcium, iron, magnesium, phosphorus, potassium, selenium, sodium, copper, manganese, zinc, fluoride. Compounds: antioxidant cartenoids such as beta-carotene, alpha-carotene, lutein, neochrome, neoxanthin, chrysanthemaxanthin, beta-cryptoxanthin, zeaxanthin, and violaxanthin; as well as the amino acids alanine, arginine, asparagine, aspartic acid, glutamic acid, glycine, histidine, isoleucine, leucine, lysine, methionine, phenylalanine, proline, serine, tryptophan, tyrosine, threonine, and valine. Also Contains: Omega 3 and 6 essential fatty acids, oleic acid, and powerful phytosterols which help lower blood cholesterol. Properties: antioxidant, anti-inflammatory. The fatty medium of an avocado increases the absorbtion of fat soluble antioxidants carotenoids by 200-400%, so the rich, healthy fats of avocado are nothing to fear. Fresh avocado is also naturally resplendent in lipase, the enzyme that break down fats.

BEE POLLEN Vitamins: A, B1, B2, B3, B5, B6, B7, B9, C, D, E, P. Minerals: calcium, magnesium, manganese, phosphorous, iron, silica, sodium, sulfur, potassium, chlorine, aluminum, copper, as well as just about everything else. Compounds: flavinoid glycosides like rutin and cartenoids such as xanthophylls, the amino acids arginine, histidine, isoleucine, leucine, methionine, phenylaline, tryptophan, valine, threonine, glutamic acid which act as precursors to HGH (human growth hormone), and nicotinic acid. Also Contains: gonadotropic and estrogenic hormones, protein, lipids, and beneficial co-enzymes. Properties: antibacterial, antioxidant, anti-cancer. Bee pollen is effective for combating anemia, asthma, ulcers, prostrate disease, obesity, kidney disorders, infertility, symptoms of menopause, fatigue, depression, cancer, colon disorders, and seasonal allergies. WOW! Soak your pollen overnight to increase its absorption factor. WARNING: if you have a history of anaphylactic reactions, proceed with caution, bee pollen can produce allergic reactions in some individuals.

BLUEBERRIES Vitamins: A, B1, B2, B3, B6, B9, B12, C, E, K. Minerals: calcium, copper, iron, manganese, magnesium, phosphorus, potassium, selenium, sodium, zinc. Compounds: anthocyanin, phenolic, pterostilbene and resveratrol. Also Contains: protein, fiber, lipids. Properties: antioxidant, rich in disease-fighting phytochemicals that prevent and even reverse serious diseases like cancer, diabetes, heart disease, stomach ulcer. In addition, blueberries also help lower cholesterol levels and increase motor cognitive functions by up to 5% in controlled studies!

BURDOCK ROOT Vitamins: B1, B2, B3, B5, B6, B9, C, E. Minerals: silicon, calcium, iron, magnesium, manganese, copper, phosphorus, selenium, zinc and potassium. Compounds: polyacetylenes, chlorogenic acid, resin and taraxosterol. Also Contains: trace EFAs, inulin, tannin, lactone, arcigen, mucilage. Properties: antibacterial, antifungal, anti-inflammatory. Burdock root assists with filtering uric acid from the blood, and has traditionally been used to treat skin conditions such as acne, eczema, psoriasis, and rashes of all kinds.

CACAO (RAW) Vitamins: A, B1, B2, B3, B5, C, E. Minerals: magnesium, calcium, iron, copper, potassium, phosphorus, manganese, selenium and zinc. Compounds: the flavinoids catechin, epicatechin, and polyphenol antioxidants such as procyandin; the alkaloid theobromine. Also Contains: the neurotransmitters serotonin, phenylethylamine, and anandamide. Properties: antioxidant, antidepressant. Raw cacao contains the highest ORAC antioxidant value of any known food, weighing in at 96,000 units. In addition to containing a number of mood enhancing compounds, cacao also contains the enzyme inhibitors that slow the breakdown of anandamide in the brain, which makes the good feelings it fosters last longer! Cacao also promotes relaxation and appears to lower blood pressure while inhibiting the blood's ability to clot, thus reducing the risk of stroke and heart attacks. If that weren't enough, cacao also increases the body's ability to metabolise sugars! Now how's that for a sinless confection?!?!?

CILANTRO Vitamins: A, B9, C, E, K. Minerals: manganese, magnesium, iron, calcium, phosphorus, potassium, sodium, copper, zinc and selenium. Compounds: dodecenol, choline, caffeic and chlorogenic acid; the carotenoids lutein, zeaxanthin, and beta-cryptoxanthin; the flavinoids quercetin, kaempferol, rhamnetin, and epigenin; and other phytonutrients like carvone, geraniol, limonene, borneol, camphor, elemol, and linalool. Also Contains: phytosterols, Omega 6 essential fatty acids, Properties: antifungal, antibacterial, antidiabetic. Also know as CORIANDER, cilantro has been found to chelate (remove) heavy metals like mercury, aluminum, and lead from the body. In fact, it is believed to cross the blood-brain barrier and actually remove said metals from the brain.

CELERY Vitamins: A, B2, B3, B5, B6, B9, C, E, K, choline, betaine. Minerals: calcium, iron, magnesium, potassium, phosphorus, sodium, selenium, manganese, zinc, flouride, molybdenum, silica. Compounds: favinoids and other phenolic antioxidant nutrients like dihydrostilbenoids lunularin; furanocoumarins like bergapten and psoralen; caffeic acid, and the amino acids tryptophan, threonine, isoleucine, leucine, lysine, methionine, cystine, phenylalanine, tyrosine, valine, arginine, histidine, alanine, aspartic acid, glutamic acid, glycine, proline, and serine. Also Contains: Omega 6 essential fatty acids and phytosterols. Properties: antioxidant, anti-inflammatory, anticancer. Celery juice has been consumed as a treatment for rashes and skin disorders for centuries, and was recently shown to be protective against colon and rectal cancers.

CHARD Vitamins: A, B1, B2, B3, B5, B6, B7, B9, C, E, K, choline, betaine. Minerals: calcium, iron, magnesium, phosphorus, potassium, sodium, manganese, iron, copper, zinc, selenium. Compounds: anthocyanin and carotenoid antioxidants, and the amino acids arginine, histidine, isoleucine, leucine, lysine, methionine, phenylalanine, threonine, valine, and tryptophan. Also Contains: Omega 3 and 6 essential fatty acids, phytosterols. Properties: anti-inflammatory. Chard is one of the most nutrient and mineral rich foods on earth. It nourishes the brain, heart, lungs, kidneys, skin and colon. Consuming 2.8 servings of a vitamin E rich green leafy vegetables a day has been shown to lower the risk of cognitive decline by 40%.

CHIA Vitamins: B3 Minerals: calcium, phosphorus, potassium, sodium, manganese, copper, zinc, iron, molybdenum. Compounds: the antioxidant flavinoid quercetin, kaempferol, myricetin, chlorogenic acid, caffeic acid, and the amino acids tryptophan, threonine, isoleucine, leucine, lysine, methionine, cystine, phenylalanine, tyrosine, valine, arginine, histidine, alanine, aspartic acid, glutamic acid, glycine, proline, and serine. Also Contains: Omega 3 and 6 essential fatty acids. Properties: anti-inflammatory, antioxidant, anticancer, antidiabetic. Not only have the antioxidants in chia been shown to be protective against various cancers, but the humble chia seed is also beneficial for individuals with diabetes. Chia slows the rate at which carbohydrates are metabolised into sugars, providing blood glucose stabilizing effects. Chia also helps control blood pressure, provide long lasting hydration for athletes when mixed with water, and their consumption helps create a low calorie "feeling of fullness" that can be an effective aid for hungry dieters.

COCONUT (MEAT) Vitamins: B1, B2, B3, B5, B6, B9, C, K, choline. Minerals: iron, magnesium, phosphorus, potassium, zinc, sodium, manganese, copper, selenium. <u>Compounds</u>: medium chain fatty acids such as caprylic acid, capric acid, lauric acid, myristic acid, and the amino acids alanine, aginine, aspartic acid, cystine, glutamic acid, histidine, leucine, lysine, proline, phenylalanine, serine, tyrosine, tryptophan, threonine, isoleucine, methionine, valine, and glycine. <u>Also Contains</u>: Omega 6 essential fatty acids, phytosterols, and naturally saturated medium chain fatty acids. <u>Properties</u>: antimicrobial, antiviral, antifungal, antibacterial, antioxidant and somewhat anti-inflammatory. It has been said that young coconut meat can restore both oxidative tissue damage and male sexual fluids.

COCONUT (OIL)

<u>Vitamins</u>: E, K, choline. <u>Minerals</u>: trace iron. <u>Also Contains</u>: Omega 6 fatty acids, phytosterols, and naturally saturated medium chain fatty acids such as caprylic acid, capric acid, lauric acid and myristic acid. <u>Properties</u>: anticancer, antioxidant, anti-genotoxic, antibacterial, antiviral, antifungal, and strong anti-inflammatory. The MCFA's in coconut oil resemble the lipid membranes of bacteria, yeast, fungi, and viruses. In the presence of MCFA's, microbes and viruses become confused as to the location of their cellular boundaries and inadvertently spill their genetic contents, making them vulnerable to white blood cells. Curiously, coconut oil reduces our need for both vitamin E and Omega 3 essential fatty acids, and lowers overall body fat accumulation while improving HDL to LDL ratios.

COCONUT (WATER)

<u>Vitamins</u>: B1, B2, B3, B5, B6, B9, C, choline. <u>Minerals</u>: calcium, magnesium, phosphorus, potassium, zinc, sodium, manganese, copper, selenium, iron. <u>Compounds</u>: the amino acids alanine, aginine, aspartic acid, cystine, glutamic acid, histidine, leucine, lysine, proline, phenylalanine, serine, tyrosine. <u>Also Contains</u>: Omega 6 essential fatty acids and medium chain fatty acids such as caprylic acid, capric acid, lauric acid and myristic acid. <u>Properties</u>: antiviral, antifungal, antibacterial, mildly anti-inflammatory, antioxidant. One of the highest sources of electrolytes in nature, young coconut water is nearly identical to human blood plasma, and is still used for blood transfusions in India today. Human blood is 55% plasma, and 45% hemoglobin.

CRANBERRIES

<u>Vitamins</u>: A, B3, B5, B6, B9, C, D, E, K, choline, betaine. <u>Minerals</u>: calcium, iron, magnesium, phosphorus, potassium, sodium, manganese, iron, copper, zinc, selenium. Compounds: carotenoid and anthocyanin antioxidants, as well as the amino acids alanine, aginine, aspartic acid, cystine, glutamic acid, histidine, leucine, lysine, proline, phenylalanine, serine, tyrosine, tryptophan, threonine, isoleucine, methionine, valine, and glycine. <u>Also Contains</u>: Omega 3 and 6 essential fatty acids. <u>Properties</u>: anti-inflammatory, anticancer, antibacterial. The proanthocyanidins (PACs) found in cranberries act as a protective barrier in both the urinary tract and the stomach lining, preventing the attachment of bacteria that can cause infections and ulcers. Cranberries have also been shown to induce apoptosis in cancer cells, making them effective against breast, colon, lung, and prostate cancers.

CUCUMBERS

<u>Vitamins</u>: A, B1, B2, B3, B5, B6, B9, C, K, choline, betaine. <u>Minerals</u>: potassium, phosphorus, magnesium, sodium, silica, calcium, selenium, iron, manganese, molybdenum, copper, zinc, and flouride. <u>Compounds</u>: ascorbic acid, caffeic acid, and the amino acids tryptophan, threo-nine, isoleucine, leucine, lysine, methionine, cystine, phenylalanine, tyrosine, valine, arginine, histidine, alanine, aspartic acid, glutamic acid, glycine, proline, and serine. <u>Also Contains</u>: Omega 3 and 6 essential fatty acids, phytosterols, and the enzyme erepsin. <u>Properties</u>: diruetic, antiparasitic. Aside from containing copious quantities of bioavailable silica, the mineral essential to the growth and repair of connective tissues, cucumbers also contain erepsin, the enzyme which digests proteins and kills parasites -- like tapeworms!

FLAXSEEDS (OIL)

<u>Vitamins</u>: B1, B2, B3, B5, B6, B9, E, choline. <u>Compounds</u>: phytoestrogens like lignans. Minerals: manganese, potassium, calcium, iron, magnesium, zinc and selenium. <u>Also Contains</u>: Omega 3, 6, and 9 essential fatty acids. <u>Properties</u>: strong anti-inflammatory. Essential fatty acids are involved in respiratory process of all cells, and are crucial to oxygen transport. EFA's affect the health of the hair, skin and nails, plus slow the oxidation of cholesterol in the bloodstream. EFA's are not dangerous fats at all. Rather they are ESSENTIAL to health and must be consumed from external sources because our bodies don't produce them.

Flaxseed oil and ground flax both supply the body with essential fatty acids that lubricate the skin, joints, and eyes, while offering protection against heart disease, high blood pressure, cancer, diabetes, constipation and arthritis.

GARLIC Vitamins: A, B1, B2, B3, B5, B6, C, E, K, choline. Minerals: calcium, iron, selenium, magnesium, potassium, phosphorus, sulphur, copper, manganese, and zinc. Compounds: the carotenoids lutein, zeaxanthin, and beta-carotene; the amino acids tryptophan, threonine, isoleucine, leucine, lysine, methionine, cystine, phenylalanine, tyrosine, valine, arginine, histidine, alanine, aspartic acid, glutamic acid, glycine, proline, and serine; and such sulphur compounds as thiosulfinates, sulfoxides, and dithiins. Also Contains: Omega 3 and 6 essential fatty acids. Properties: antibacterial, antiviral, antifungal, anticancer, antioxidant, and super-duper strong anti-inflammatory powers. Mankind's cure-all for thousands of years, garlic possesses pharmacological benefits such as blood sugar regulation and general prevention against heart disease (it inhibits the formation of arterial plaque). Due to its high sulphur content, garlic has been shown to be the most profound anticancer food around and can slow the growth of tumors! EAT IT ON EVERYTHING!!!

GINGER Vitamins: B1, B2, B3, B5, B6, B9, C, E. Minerals: calcium, iron, magnesium, potassium, phosphorus, zinc, copper, manganese, selenium. Compounds: gingerols, and the amino acids threonine, isoleucine, leucine, lysine, phenylalanine, valine, arginine, histidine, alanine, aspartic acid, glutamic acid, glycine, proline, and serine. Also Contains: Omega 3 and 6 essential fatty acids. Properties: antispasmodic, anti-nausea, anti-emitic, anti-inflammatory, anticancer, antioxidant. Mankind's other historic cure-all, ginger not only boosts the entire immune system, but studies have shown that it effectively treats arthritis, nausea, colorectal cancer, and even induces death in ovarian cancer cells. EAT IT ON EVERYTHING!!!

GOJI "WOLF" BERRIES Vitamins: A, B1, B2, B3, B5, B6, B7, C, E, betaine. Minerals: calcium, iron, phosphorus, potassium, chromium, zinc, magnesium, copper, sodium, selenium, germanium. Compounds: carotenoids lutein, lycopene, cryptoxanthin, xanthophyll, zeaxanthin, beta-carotene; sesquiterpenoids, tetraterpenoids; and high doses of the amino acids tryptophan, threonine, isoleucine, leucine, lysine, methionine, cystine, phenylalanine, tyrosine, valine, arginine, histidine, alanine, aspartic acid, glutamic acid, glycine, proline, and serine. Also contains: Omega 3 and 6 essential fatty acids, monosaccharides and polysaccharides, and phytosterols like beta-sisterol. Properties: anticancer, antioxidant, anti-inflammatory. When consumed on a regular basis, theses berries have been historically found to increase longevity and promote excellent health. They balance blood sugar levels and increase the production of red cells, white cells, platelets, and lymphocyte activity. A study in Japan found the consumption of goji berries to inhibit tumor growth by 58%. One polysaccharide found in goji berries has proved to stimulate the pituitary secretion of human growth hormone.

HONEY (RAW) Vitamins: B2, B3, B5, B6, B9, B12, C, K, choline, betaine. Minerals: calcium, phosphorus, iron, copper, potassium, magnesium, manganese, silicoa, sulphur, sodium, titanium, zinc, iodine, chlorine, boron, molybdenum. Compounds: the phytonutrients caffeic acid, methyl caffeate, phenylethyl caffeate, and phenylethyl dimethylcaffeate -- which have been shown to prevent colon cancer in animals; and the amino acids tryptophan, leucine, lysine, isoleucine, methionine, cystiene, thresonine, arginine, phenylalanine, histidine, valine, glutamic acid, tyrosine, glycine, serine, proline, alanine, aspartic acid, hydroxyproline, and butyric acid. Also Contains: 2% protein, probiotics lactobacilli and bifidobacteria, and lots of neat enzymes, including glucose oxidase which produces hydrogen peroxide when combined with water. Properties: antibacterial, antiviral, antifungal, antioxidant and all around anti-carcinogenic. Honey contains a 1:1 ratio of fructose to glucose, making it a perfect sugar for your liver to metabolize into glycogen. Gylcogen feeds the brain during sleep and exercise, and when glycogen levels drop, the brain triggers the release of stress hormones adrenaline and cortisol. While honey may be high on the glycemic index, this isn't necessarily a bad thing -- its sugars are processed efficiently and honey has been shown to assist in the regulation of blood sugar and the inhibition of candida and yeast infections. Honey also out-performs over the counter cough suppressants and is fantastic as an antiseptic healing agent when applied topically.

INCA "GOLDEN" BERRIES
Vitamins: A, B1, B2, B6, B12, C. Minerals: phosphorus. Compounds: flavinoids and carotenoids. Also Contains: 16% protein, pectin, and secretory IgA, a plant antibody which strengthens the immune system. Properties: mild laxative, anti-sclerotic, antiviral, anticancer, anti-inflammatory, antihistamine, and antioxidant. Notorious for it's ability to regulate the rate at which food moves through the 30 foot tube (thus preventing surges in blood glucose levels), the pectin found in Inca berries also works wonders when it comes to lowering LDL cholesterol. Because of the effects the berry's flavinoids produce in preventing the accumulation of arterial plaque, Inca berries are an excellent blood toner for anyone challenged with high blood pressure, diabetes, or heart disease.

KALE
Vitamins: A, B1, B2, B3, B5, B6, B9, C, K. Minerals: sodium, calcium, iron, manganese, potassium, phosphorus, zinc, copper, magnesium, selenium. Compounds: the 9 essential amino acids histidine, isoleucine, leucine, lysine, methionine, phenylalanine, threonine, phenylalanine, tryptophan, valine, as well as phytonutrient glucosinolates and methyl cysteine sulfoxides. Also Contains: Omega 3 and 6 essential fatty acids. Properties: anti-inflammatory, anticancer, antidiabetic, antimicrobial and antioxidant. When RAW leaves of kale are chopped or chewed, a compound called sulforaphane is formed. This compound has been shown to inhibit the growth of chemically induced breast cancers, and can even cause colon cancer cells to commit suicide. Sulforaphane induces the liver to produce phase 2 enzymes, which have a profound ability to detoxify cancer causing chemicals.

MACA ROOT (POWDER)
Vitamins: B1, B2, B3, B6, B12, C, E. Minerals: calcium, potassium, copper, zinc, iron, manganese, magnesium, phosphorus, potassium, iodine, sodium, zinc. Compounds: glucosinolates, 4 novel alkaloids: macaina 1, 2, 3, and 4 (which are responsible for activating hormone regulators located in the brain); saponins, tannins, p-methoxybenzyl isothiocyanate (a known aphrodesiac), beta-ecdysone; and the amino acids alanine, arginine, serine, histidine, aspartic acid, glutamic acid, glycine, valine, phenylalanine, tyrosine, leucine, serine, HO-proline, isoleucine, lysine, methionine, proline, sarcosine, tryptophan, and threonine. Also Contains: Omega 6 and 9 essential fatty acids, sitosterols, stigmasterol, and palmitic acid. Properties: hormone balancing, mood stabilizing. Maca is a cruciferous root vegetable indigenous to South America that balances your endocrine system by stimulating and nourishing the pituitary and hypothalamus -- the master glands. In turn, these glands regulate the rest of the endocrine system, including the thyroid, adrenal glands, pancreas, and sexual organs. In addition, maca also supports the manufacture of neurotransmitters like dopamine and noradrenaline, two substances that play a major role in mental function, sexual function, stamina and arousal. Maca is often used as a coffee subsititute for the "enegery boost" it provides, and is traditionally made into sweet drinks and puddings.

MACADAMIA NUTS
Vitamins: B1, B2, B3, B5, B9, C, E. Minerals: potassium, phosphorus, magnesium, calcium, manganese, copper, sodium, selenium, zinc. Compounds: phenolic compounds such as flavonoids, phytoestrogens, phytic acid, tannins, saponins, and lignans. Also Contains: richest food source of Omega 9 essential fatty acid, palmitic & oleic acids. Properties: antioxidant. Rich in monounsaturated fats, macadamia nuts have the ability to reduce LDL levels while boosting HDL levels in the bloodstream when eaten daily. 80% oil, macadamias have long held beautifying and healing properties for the skin.

MESQUITE
Vitamins: C. Minerals: barium, boron, calcium, chromium, cobalt, copper, iron, magnesium, manganese, molybdenum, phosphorus, potassium, sodium, sulfur, zinc. Compounds: lysine. Also Contains: 16% protein, fiber. Properties: antidiabetic. A traditional Native American staple made by grinding seed pods from the mesquite tree into a fine meal, mesquite contains a range of minerals and trace minerals. Mesquite requires no insulin to digest, and therefore helps to maintain constant blood sugar levels.

MINERAL MANNA
Minerals: silicon, barium, nickel, aluminum, fluorine, neodymium, iron, copper, praseodymium, magnesium, vanadium, gallium, potassium, zirconium, cadmium, calcium, manganese, lithium, sulphur, zinc, molybdenum, sodium, cerium, boron, titanium, rubidium, scandium, phosphorus, and many, many other trace minerals. Coumpounds: Many of the afforementioned

minerals come in the form of compounds like "aluminosillicate," which are totally harmless. Also contains: electrolytes, beneficial microbes, angstrom "ormus" elements, humic/fulvic substances. Properties: heavy metal chelative, detoxifying, immune boosting, mood stabilizing, radioactivity protective, promotes physical stamina. "Mineral Manna" is a blend of pyrophillite clay, humic/ fulvic substances, magnesium dense ancient plant minerals, Himalayan salt, and "ormalite" -- which is a clay comprised of single atom state elements (smaller than ionic or colloidal) capable of providing acute mineral nutrition to your brain and nervous system. The high silicon content of the clays in Mineral Manna have an affinity for bonding with heavy metals (even in the human body) to create non-toxic compounds.

OLIVES Vitamins: A, B3, B5, B6, C, E, K. Minerals: calcium, magnesium, manganese, copper, iron, phosphorus, potassium, selenium, sodium, zinc. Compounds: essential amino acids histidine, iso- leucine, leucine, lysine, methionine, phenylalanine, threonine, phenylalanine, valine; tyrosine, aspartic acid, and glutaminic acid, polyphenols, anthocyanins, monounsaturated fats, and squa- lene. Also Contains: Omega 3 and 6 essential fatty acids, Properties: antioxidant, anti-inflam- matory. Olives contain a profound amount of bioavailable vitamin E, which acts as a powerful anticancer agent in several different arenas of the body, ranging from the heart to the colon. An unsaturated oxygen carrier, squalene is popular in many skin products for its ability to smooth the skin. In its underived form, squalene stimulates the immune system.

RADISHES Vitamins: A, B1, B2, B3, B4, B6, B8, B9, C, K. Minerals: copper, manganese, potas- sium calcium, magnesium, iron, phosphorous, zinc, selenium, flouride, sulphur, silicon, sodium. Compounds: raphanin, phytosterols, and the 9 essential amino acids histidine, isoleucine, leu- cine, lysine, methionine, phenylalanine, threonine, phenylalanine, tryptophan, and valine. Also Contains: protein, and Omega 3 and 6 essential fatty acids. Properties: diruetic. Throughout his- tory radishes have been effective when used as a medicinal food for liver and kidney disorders. They contain a variety of sulfur-based phytochemicals that stimulate the liver to increase the flow of bile. Radishes also work to dissolve kidney stones and alleviate the pain associated with them. Moreover, raphanin in radishes balances thyroid hormones, which help maintain an ideal body weight.

SPIRULINA Vitamins: A, B1, B2, B3, B5, B6, B7, B8, B9, B12, E. Minerals: iron, calcium, zinc, potas- sium, magnesium, manganese, selenium, phosphorus. Compounds: the carotenoids alpha-carotene, beta-carotene, xanthophylis, cryptoxanthin, echinenone, zeaxanthin, lutein; the amino acids alanine, arginine, serine, histidine, aspartic acid, glutamic acid, glycine, valine, phenylala- nine, tyrosine, leucine, serine, isoleucine, lysine, methionine, proline, sarcosine, tryptophan, and threonine; and antioxidant pigments phycocyanin, porphyrin, phycoerythrin, tetrapyrrole, and phytonadione, as well as chlorophyll. Also Contains: Omega 6 (including the super-good-for- you-gamma-linolenic or GLA) and 9 essential fatty acids, nucleic acids RNA and DNA. Properties: Antioxidant, anticancer, immune boosting. Spirulina is a blue green microalgae, and one of the oldest living life forms on earth. It's believed that blue-green algae (like spirulina) is res- ponisble in part for producing the world's oxygen supply, which set the stage for the evolution of other life forms by both creating the worlds habitat, and forming the base of the food chain. Spirulina is a low calorie, high protein, vita-mineral rich food that packs a helluva lot of bang for its buck. It is also one of the richest sources of chlorophyll in nature. Blue green algae has been a staple in the diets of many, many, many creatures large and small (including humans) since life on earth began billions of years ago.

WATERCRESS Vitamins: A, B1, B2, B3, B5, B6, B9, B12, C, E, K. Minerals: iron, calcium, potassium, magnesium, manganese, sodium, copper, iodine, selenium, fluoride, phosphorus, zinc. Compounds: the amino acids proline, tryptophan, threonine, isoleucine, leucine, lysine, methionine, phenyl- alanine, cystine, valine, arginine, histidine, tyrosine, alanine, aspartic acid, glutamic acid, glycine and serine; chlorophyll. Properties: anticancer, diuretic, antioxidant, expectorant. The compounds found in watercress are known chemopreventive agents for many forms of breast cancer!!!! Watercress is in the Brassicaceae family of vegetables, along with cabbage, collard, and broccoli -- all of which have profound anticancer properties. Watercress can be harvested wild, and is one of the oldest known leafy greens consumed by humans. Eat it up!!

Leaf...

Pool Your Resources

tissue...

B.

bacteria...

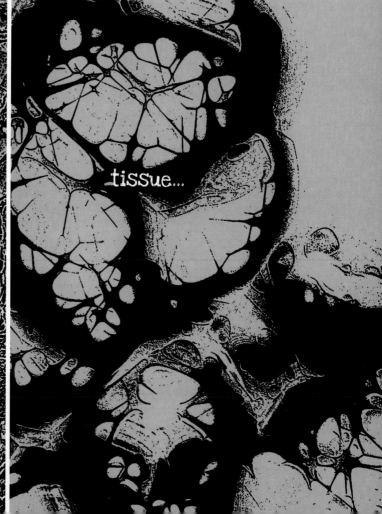

Branch out and CONNECT!

NUTRITIONAL PRODUCTS, COMMUNITY & MORE INFO:

www.therawfoodworld.com
www.davidwolfe.com
www.infinitygreens.com
www.vitalityherbsandclay.com
greensmoothiecommunity.com
www.e3live.com
essentiallivingfoods.com
www.ripestcherry.com
healthforce.com
thebestdayever.com
www.reneeloux.com
www.rawguru.com
www.ancientsunnutrition.com
www.oneluckyduck.com
www.aniphyo.com

RETREATS & CLEANSING OPPORTUNITIES:

The Ashram Retreat
www.theashram.com
818.222.6900

Hippocrates Health Institute
www.hippocratesinst.org
888.228.1755

Tree of Life Rejuvenation Center
www.treeoflife.nu
866.394.2520

Lumeria Maui
www.lumeriamaui.com
855.579.8877

RECOMMENDED READS:

There is a Cure for Diabetes: The 21-Day+ Program
by Gabriel Cousens, MD

Enzyme Nutrition: The Food Enzyme Concept
by Dr. Edward Howell

Anticancer: A New Way of Life
by David Servan-Schreiber, MD, PhD

The Sunfood Diet Success System
by David Wolfe

Food Combining Made Easy
by Herbert M. Shelton

The Wheatgrass Book
by Anne Wigmore

river.

Need a Good Reference?

ENDNOTES

{ *In addition to the following citations, sources for the*
SUPER NUTRITION APPENDIX also include: nutritiondata.self.com,
www.whfoods.com, nutritionfacts.org, and livestrong.org. }

1. Renée Loux Underkoffler, <u>Living Cuisine: The Art and Spirit of Raw Foods</u>. (New York: Avery, 2003), 209.

2. Rosemary Richardson, "Plant Growth Regulators," Belleview College, 23 Apr. 2011, 14 |lecture notes online|; available from http://scidiv.bellevuecollege.edu/rkr/Biology213/lectures/pdfs/Hormones213.pdf

3. Ibid.

4. Gary Null, <u>The Complete Encyclopedia of Natural Healing: A Comprehensive A-Z Listing of Common and Chronic Illnesses and Their Proven Natural Treatments</u>. "Quotes About Alkaline Foods from the World's Top Natural Health / Natural Living Authors," Natural News Naturalpedia, n.d. |quote online|; available from http://www.naturalpedia.com/alkaline_foods.html.

5. Amy Kreydin, "Traditional Chinese medicine: Fall Season," Examiner, 31 Mar. 2009 |article online|; available from http://www.examiner.com/article/traditional-chinese-medicine-fall-season.

6. Ibid.

7. Steven Sonmore, "Enjoy the Energy of Fall: Autumn and Traditional Chinese Medicine," Acufinder, n.d. |article online|; available from https://www.acufinder.com/Acupuncture+Information/Detail/Enjoy+the+Energy+of+Fall+Autumn+and+Traditional+Chinese+Medicine

8. Larry Stoler, "Changing With The Seasons," Whole Health Chicago, 22 Sep. 2011 |article online|; available from http://wholehealthchicago.wordpress.com/2011/09/22/changing-with-the-seasons/

9. Ronald Hoffman, "Update on Cancer," Dr. Ronald Hoffman, n.d. |article online|; available from http://www.drhoffman.com/page.cfm/602

10. "Antioxidants and Cancer Prevention: Fact Sheet," National Cancer Institute, 28 Jul. 2004 |article online|; available from http://www.cancer.gov/cancertopics/factsheet/prevention/antioxidants

11. Helmut Sies and Wilhelm Stahl, "Vitamins E and C, Beta-Carotene, and Other Carotenoids as Antioxidants," <u>American Journal of Clinical Nutrition</u> Dec. 1995, 1319S |article online|; available from http://ajcn.nutrition.org/content/62/6/1315S.full.pdf+html

12. "Vitamins and Minerals: Understanding Their Role," Helpguide.org, Educational Supplement from <u>Harvard Health Publications</u>, n.d. |article online|; available from http://www.helpguide.org/harvard/vitamins_and_minerals.htm

13. Helen Kollias, "To Every Food There Is A Season," Precision Nutrition, 21 Aug. 2009 |article online|; available from http://www.precisionnutrition.com/seasonal-food

14. "About Us," Slow Food, n.d. |description online|; available from http://www.slowfood.com/international/1/about-us?-session=query_session:4CF0A9411d5f8077BDyTA12067D5

15. Eric Schlosser, <u>Fast Food Nation: The Dark Side of the All-American Meal</u>, first Mariner Books edition 2012 (New York: Houghton Mifflin Company, 2012), 124.

16. Annie Jubb and David Jubb, <u>The LifeFood Recipe Book</u>, revised Spring 1998 (New York: Excellence Inc.), 6.

17. F. Stuart Chapin, III, "The Mineral Nutrition of Wild Plants," <u>Annual Review of Ecology and Systematics</u> 11 (1980), 246 |article online|; available from http://links.jstor.org/sici?sici=0066-4162%281980%2911%3C233%3ATMNOWP%3E2.0.CO%3B2-P

18. "The Use of Bee Pollen as a Superfood," Mercola, n.d. |article online|; available from http://www.mercola.com/article/diet/bee_pollen.htm

19. Ibid.

20. Donna Rae, "Protect Your Family From Radiation Exposure with Superfoods" NaturalNews Network, 24 Apr. 2011, |article online|; available from http://www.naturalnews.com/032162_superfoods_radiation_exposure.html

21. William Robinson, "Delay in the Appearance of Palpable Mammary Tumors in C3H Mice Following the Ingestion of Pollenized Food," <u>Journal of the National Cancer Institute</u>, 9(2) Oct. 1948, 119-123

22. David Wolfe, <u>The Sunfood Diet Success System</u>, 7th Edition (San Diego: Sunfood Publishing, 2008), 289.

23. Ibid.

24. Ibid, 541-554.

25. Underkoffler, ibid, 102-103.

26. David Wolfe and Shazzie, <u>Naked Chocolate</u> (San Diego: Maul Brothers Publishing, 2005), 60-71.

27. Danica Collins, "Benefits of the Goji Berry," Underground Health Reporter, n.d. |article online|; available from http://undergroundhealthreporter.com/goji-berry-benefits#axzz2B1W0czPQ

28. The George Mateljan Foundation for The World's Healthiest Foods, "Avocados," n.d. |article online|; available from http://www.whfoods.com/genpage.php?tname=foodspice&dbid=5

29. "Avocados," ibid.

30. Genetics Home Reference, "Leucine," Glossary, 12 Nov. 2012, |definition online|; available from http://ghr.nlm.nih.gov/glossary=leucine

31. Jeff S. Volek, "Leucine Triggers Muscle Growth," Nutrition Express, n.d. |article online|; available from http://www.nutritionexpress.com/article+index/authors/jeff+s+volek+phd+rd/showarticle.aspx?articleid=807

32. Edward Howell, <u>Enzyme Nutrition: The Food Enzyme Concept</u> (Wayne: Avery Publishing Group, 1985), 33.

33. Stephen Blauer, "Introduction," in Edward Howell, <u>Enzyme Nutrition: The Food Enzyme Concept</u>, ix.

34. Ibid.

35. Edward Howell, 147.

36. Ibid, 35.

37. Ibid, 81.

38. Francis M. Pottenger, Jr., <u>Pottenger's Cats: A Study in Nutrition</u>, 2nd Edition (La Mesa: Price-Pottenger Nutrition Foundation, 2009).

39. Ibid, 3.

40. E3Live® (Original) - 16oz, "Benefits," E3Live, n.d. [product description online]; available from http://www.e3live.com/all_products/e3live.html?SID=d9fa9c467488cf5b9422816ee967078c

41. Gitte S. Jensen, Donald I. Ginsberg, Christian Drapeau, "Blue-Green Algae as an Immuno-Enhancer and Biomodulator," <u>The Journal of the American Nutraceutical Association</u>, 3(4) (Winter 2001), 24 [article online]; available from http://www.ancientsuninc.com/AFAarticlebiomodenhancer.pdf

42. Christian Drapeau, excerpts from <u>Primordial Food: A Wild Blue-Green Algae with Unique Health Properties</u>, Ancient Sun Nutrition, n.d. [article online]; available from http://www.ancientsunnutrition.com/category/articles.primordialfoodexcerpts/

43. Ahma Belay, "The Potential Application of Spirulina (Arthrospira) as a Nutritional and Therapeutic Supplement in Health Management," <u>The Journal of the American Nutraceutical Association</u>, 5(2) (Spring 2002), 32 [article online]; available from http://www.ana-jana.org/reprints/spirulinareprint.pdf

44. Marylin Light, "Burdock," Dr. Christopher's Herbal Legacy, n.d. [article online]; available from http://www.herbal-legacy.com/Light_Medicinal.html

45. Greg Kelly, "Inulin-Type Prebiotics - A Review: Part 1," <u>Alternative Medicine Review</u> 13(4) (2008), 315-316 [article online]; available from http://www.altmedrev.com/publications/13/4/315.pdf

46. "Maitake Mushroom," American Cancer Society, n.d. [article online]; available from http://www.cancer.org/Treatment/TreatmentsandSideEffects/ComplementaryandAlternativeMedicine/DietandNutrition/maitake-mushrooms

47. Ibid.

48. Gretchen Cuda-Kroen, "Baby's Palate And Food Memories Shaped Before Birth" NPR, 8 Aug. 2011 [article online]; available from http://www.npr.org/2011/08/08/139033757/babys-palate-and-food-memories-shaped-before-birth

49. Schlosser, 123.

50. Russell L. Blaylock, "Excitotoxins, Neurodegeneration and Neurodevelopment," The Medical Sentinel Journal, n.d., 1 [article online]; available from http://landofpuregold.com/the-pdfs/Excitotoxins.pdf

51. Ibid.

52. Ibid.

53. Schlosser, 125-126

54. Schlosser, 126-127

55. Michael Pollan, <u>The Botany of Desire: A Plant's Eye View of the World</u>, 2002 Random House Trade Paperback edition (New York: Random House, 2002), 19.

56. "Eating Oat Beta-glucan Regularly Helps Maintain Normal Blood Cholesterol," The European Food Information Council, n.d. [article online]; available from http://www.eufic.org/page/en/show/latest-science-news/fftid/Eating-oat-beta-glucan-regularly-helps-maintain-normal-blood-cholesterol/

57. The George Mateljan Foundation for The World's Healthiest Foods, "Oats," n.d. [article online]; available from http://www.whfoods.com/genpage.php?tname=foodspice&dbid=54

58. Ibid.

59. "Molecular Biology of Diindolylmethane," Diindolylmethane (DIM) Information Resource Center, n.d. [article online]; available from http://www.diindolylmethane.org/molecular_biology.htm

60. Barbara Ann Karmanos Cancer Institute, "Diindolylmethane in Treating Patients With Stage I or Stage II Prostate Cancer Undergoing Radical Prostatectomy," ClinicalTrials.gov, 3 Dec. 2o12 [study record detail online]; available from http://clinicaltrials.gov/ct2/show/NCT00888654

61. Self Nutrition Data, "Collard Greens," Nutrition Facts, n.d. [facts and summary online]; available from http://nutritiondata.self.com/facts/vegetables-and-vegetable-products/2410/2

62. Cathryn Couch and JoEllen DeNicola, <u>Nourishing Connections Cookbook: The Healing Power of Food & Community</u>, 2nd Edition (Marin: The Ceres Community Project, 2011), 34 [PDF online]; available from http://ceresproject.org/cookbook/NCPDFs/01_Chapter1_NutritionBasics.pdf

63. Gabriel Cousens, edited by Nonnie Chrystal, "Iodine - The Universal & Holistic Super Mineral," Patrick Timpone's One Radio Network, 3 Mar. 2013, [article online]; available from http://oneradionetwork.com/newsflash/iodine-the-universal-holistic-super-mineral-article/

64. Theodore T Zava and David T Zava, "Assessment of Japanese Iodine Intake Based on Seaweed Consumption in Japan: A Literature-Based Analysis," <u>Thyroid Research</u> 4(14) 5 Oct. 2011 [article online]; available from http://www.thyroidresearch-journal.com/content/4/1/14

65. Couch and DeNicola, ibid.

66. Jane Teas, et al., "Dietary Seaweed Modifies Estrogen and Phytoestrogen Metabolism in Healthy Postmenopausal Women," <u>The Journal of Nutrition</u>, 139(5) May 2009, 943 [PDF online]; available from http://jn.nutrition.org/content/139/5/939.full.pdf+html

67. Pearson Schools and FE Colleges, "A2 Biology Unit 1 Module 4: Respiration (Student Book)" <u>OCR A Level Sciences</u>, n.d., 80 [PDF textbook online]; available from http://www.pearsonschoolsandfecolleges.co.uk/AssetsLibrary/SECTORS/Secondary/PDFs/Science/HeinemannScience/OCRALevelSampleLessons/OCRA2Biology_StudentBook9780435691905_Unit1Module4.pdf

68. Ibid.

69. Anna Taran, "Length of the Human Alimentary Canal," The Physics Factbook: An Encyclopedia of Scientific Essays, edited by Glenn Elert, 2001 [essay online]; available from http://hypertextbook.com/facts/2001/AnnaTaran.shtml

70. Ibid.

71. The George Mateljan Foundation for The World's Healthiest Foods, "Does the Number of Times I Chew My Food Impact My Digestion?," n.d. [article online]; available from http://www.whfoods.com/genpage.php?tname=george&dbid=36

72. Ibid.

73. Taran, ibid.

74. L. Lemmens, S. Van Buggenhout, A.M. Van Loey, and M.E. Hendrickx, "Particle Size Reduction Leading to Cell Wall Rupture is More important for the beta-carotene bioaccessibility of raw compared to thermally processed carrots," Journal of Agricultural and Food Chemistry, 58(24) 22 Dec. 2010, 12769-76 [abstract online]; available from http://www.ncbi.nlm.nih.gov/pubmed/21121612

75. Bridget A. Cassady, et. al., "Mastication of Almonds: Effects of Lipid Bioaccessibility, Appetite, and Hormone Response," American Journal of Clinical Nutrition, 89(3) Mar. 2009, 794-800 [PDF article online]; available from http://ajcn.nutrition.org/content/89/3/794.full.pdf+html

76. Wayne Coates, "Chia - Basic Facts," Azchia.com, n.d. [fact sheet online]; available from http://www.azchia.com/chia_facts.htm

77. Fitday, "The Nutrition of Chia," n.d. [article online]; available from http://www.fitday.com/fitness-articles/nutrition/healthy-eating/the-nutrition-of-chia.html#b

78. The George Mateljan Foundation for The World's Healthiest Foods, "Yams," n.d. [article online]; available from http://www.whfoods.com/genpage.php?tname=george&dbid=36

79. David Wolfe, Eating For Beauty, Second Edition (San Diego: Maul Brothers Publishing, 2003), 44.

80. The George Mateljan Foundation for The World's Healthiest Foods, "Yams," ibid.

81. E. Lund, "Non-nutritive Bioactive Constituents of Plants: Dietary Sources and Health Benefits of Glucosinolates," International Journal for Vitamin and Nutrition Research, 73(2) Mar. 2003, 135-43 [abstract online]; available from http://www.ncbi.nlm.nih.gov/pubmed/12747221

82. Christine Houghton, "The Sulphoraphane Story - Q&A" [presentation online]; available from http://www.stephenchandmd.com/Portals/0/04%20D%20AMGeneX%20Sulphoraphane%20FAQ.pdf

83. Allison Pledgie-Tracy, Michele D. Sobolewski and Nancy E. Davidson, "Sulforaphane Induces Cell Type-Specific Apoptosis in Human Breast Cancer Cell Lines," Molecular Cancer Therapeutics, (6) Mar. 2007, 1013 [PDF article online]; available from http://mct.aacrjournals.org/content/6/3/1013.full.pdf+html

84. Janelle Mayer, "Food Combining Explored: How Your Food Pairings May be Affecting Your Digestion and Health," Localblu, 16 Jul. 2012 [article online]; available from http://localblu.com/2012/07/food-combining-explored-how-your-food-pairings-may-be-affecting-your-digestion-and-health/#more-337%207

85. "Trophology," The Free Dictionary by Farlex, 2008 [medical definition online]; available from http://www.thefreedictionary.com/trophology

86. Monica Reinagel, "Food Combining Myths," Nutrition Diva, Episode 34, 2 Mar. 2012 [article online]; available from http://nutritiondiva.quickanddirtytips.com/food-combining-myths.aspx

87. August McLaughlin, "Food Combining Myths," Livestrong.com, 7 Dec. 2010 [article online]; available from http://www.livestrong.com/article/328031-food-combining-myths/

88. Herbert M. Shelton, The Hygienic System: Vol. II, Orthotrophy, Sixth Edition (San Antonio: Dr. Shelton's Health School, 1975), Chapter 26, Correct Food Combining [scan online]; available from http://www.soilandhealth.org/02/0201hyglibcat/020126shelton.orthotrophy/020126.toc.html

89. Herbert M. Shelton, Food Combining Made Easy, Thirty-First Printing, 1979 (San Antonio: Dr. Shelton's Health School, 1951) [PDF online]; available from http://www.soilandhealth.org/02/0201hyglibcat/020195.shelton.combining.pdf

90. Shelton, The Hygienic System: Vol. II, Orthotrophy, ibid.

91. Tara Alder, "Proper Food Combining," Alder Brooke Healing Arts, n.d. [article online]; available from http://www.alderbrooke.com/combine.php

92. Dennis Nelson, "The Natural Hygiene Life Science Course," Living Nutrition Magazine, Living Nutrition Publications (16), n.d. [article online]; available from http://rawglow.com/foodcombining.htm

93. Shelton, The Hygienic System: Vol. II, Orthotrophy, ibid.

94. William Howard Hay, Health Via Food, Fifth Printing, Jan. 1932 (East Aurora: Sun Diet Health Service, 1929), Chapter XVI. The Mechanism Of Digestion [scan online]; available from http://chestofbooks.com/health/nutrition/Health-via-Food/Chapter-XVI-The-Mechanism-Of-Digestion.html#.UMVdJo74Yne

95. Alder, ibid.

96. Nelson, ibid.

97. David Klein, "Food Combining For Optimum Digestion," in The Natural Hygiene Life Science Course by Dennis Nelson, Living Nutrition Magazine, Living Nutrition Publications (16), n.d. [article online]; available from http://rawglow.com/foodcombining.htm

98. R. Bowen, "Gastrointestinal Transit: How Long Does It Take?," Pathophysiology of the Digestive System, Control of Digestive System Function, 27 May 2006 Colorado State University, 27 May 2006 [article online]; available from http://www.vivo.colostate.edu/hbooks/pathphys/digestion/basics/transit.html

99. Tara Alder, "The Divine Way to Combine: Quick Reference Charts," Alder Brooke Healing Arts, n.d., Chart Front [chart online]; available from http://www.alderbrooke.com/chart.php

100. Andrew Weil, "Stumped by Oxidative Stress?" Q & A Library, Drweil.com, Weil Lifestyle, 17 Mar. 2009 [answer online]; available from http://www.drweil.com/drw/u/QAA400537/Stumped-by-Oxidative-Stress.html

101. Lawrence J. Machlin and Adrianne Bendich, "Free Radical Tissue Damage: Protective Role of Antioxidant Nutrients," The FASEB Journal, 6(1) Dec. 1987, 441-445 [article online]; available from http://www.fasebj.org/content/1/6/441.full.pdf+html

102. Brunswick Laboratories MA, USA, "Antioxidant Rating (ORAC), Per 100 g," U.S. Department of Agriculture, Journal of the American Chemical Society, data reposted in Raw Cacao, Chocolate and ORAC, Best Superfoods, blog by Transition Nutrition, 14 Aug. 2008 [blog online]; available from http://bestsuperfoods.wordpress.com/2008/08/14/raw-cacao-chocolate-and-orac/

103. Wolfe, <u>Eating for Beauty</u>, ibid, 45-67.

104. Suzanne Colston-Lynch, Tipper Lewis, and Pat Thomas, "A Botanical Boost to Immunity," Neal's Yard Remedies Natural News, 4 Oct. 2012 |article online|; available from http://www.nyrnaturalnews.com/article/a-botanical-boost-to-immunity/

105. Edward F. Group III, "The Benefits of Apple Cider Vinegar," Natural Health Blog, blog by Global Healing Center, 4 Aug. 2008 |article online|; available from http://www.globalhealingcenter.com/natural-health/the-benefits-of-apple-cider-vinegar/

106. Wolfe, <u>Eating for Beauty</u>, ibid, 37-44.

107. Ibid.

108. Kathy Preston, "Can A Plant-Based Diet Cure Cancer?" Oprah.com, 23 Oct. 2009 |article online|; available from http://www.oprah.com/health/Can-a-Plant-Based-Diet-Cure-Cancer

109. Takeshi Furuichi and Jo Myers Thompson, <u>The Bonobos: Behavior, Ecology, and Conservation</u>, (New York: Spinger Science+Business Media, 2008) 1 |excerpt online|; available from http://books.google.com/books?id=3fL1P0DpFlsC&pg=PA1&lpg=PA1&dq=Sibley+and+Ahlquist+%5B1987%5D+bonobos&source=bl&ots=qVmXO-WymT&sig=1NOks7hZw47Y7WES9qob96E7S6Q&hl=en&sa=X&ei=pgfGUNeUA-jB2QXttICYCw&ved=0CE8Q6AEwBQ#v=onepage&q=Sibley%20and%20Ahlquist%20%5B1987%5D%20bonobos&f=false

110. Michael Hofreiter, et al., "Vertebrate DNA in Fecal Samples from Bonobos and Gorillas: Evidence for Meat Consumption or Artefact?," PLoS ONE, www.plosone.org, 5(2) Feb. 2010, e9419 |article online|; available from http://www.plosone.org/article/info:doi/10.1371/journal.pone.0009419

111. Milton R. Mills, "The Comparative Anatomy Of Eating," Vegsource.com, 21 Nov. 2009 |article online|; available from http://www.vegsource.com/news/2009/11/the-comparative-anatomy-of-eating.html

112. Ibid.

113. Ibid.

114. Ibid.

115. Michaela Hau and Martin Wikelski, "Darwin's Finches," Encyclopedia of Life Sciences (eLS) (Chichester: John Wiley & Sons Ltd) Apr. 2001, 4 |reprint online|; available from http://www.princeton.edu/~hau/ReprintLinks/Darwin_Finches.pdf

116. Ibid.

117. Heidi Ledford, "Evolution Caught in the Act" Nature.com, 13 Jul. 2006 |article online|; available from http://www.nature.com/news/2006/060710/full/news060710-11.html

118. Ibid.

119. The George Mateljan Foundation for The World's Healthiest Foods, "Lycopene," n.d. |article online|; available from http://www.whfoods.com/genpage.php?tname=nutrient&dbid=121

120. Mary G. Enig, "The Latest Studies on Coconut Oil," Natural Health Strategies, n.d. |article online|; available from http://www.naturalhealthstrategies.com/heart-disease-prevention.html

121. P. Trinidad, et al., "The Cholesterol-Lowering Effect of Coconut Flakes in Humans with Moderately Raised Serum Cholesterol," <u>Journal of Medicinal Food</u>, 7(2) June 2004, 136-140 |excerpt online|; available from http://inhumanexperiment.blogspot.com/2008/12/coconut-lowers-ldl-vldl-and.html

122. Jennette Turner, "Increasing Health and Immunity with Tropical Oils," Jennette Turner Natural Foods Education, n.d |article online|; available from http://www.jennette-turner.com/publications.cfm?id=7

123. Micleu, Cindy "Nourishing the Center: Restoring Digestive Health with Fermented Foods" Jade Institute, n.d. |article online|; available from http://www.jadeinstitute.com/jade/restoring-digestive-health-with-fermented-foods.php

124. Rial D. Rolfe, "The Role of Probiotic Cultures in the Control of Gastrointestinal Health," <u>The Journal of Nutrition</u> 130(2) (2000): 396S-402S |PDF online|; available from http://jn.nutrition.org/content/130/2/396S.full.pdf+html

125. Coscia, Grace Suh "Can Pickles, Sauerkraut and Fermented Foods Make You Healthier?" The Huffington Post, Huffingtonpost.com (1 Feb. 2012) |article online|; available from http://www.huffingtonpost.com/grace-suh-coscia-lac-diplom/fermented-foods_b_1220756.html

126. Rolfe, ibid.

127. The George Mateljan Foundation for The World's Healthiest Foods, "Sesame seeds," n.d. |article online|; available from http://www.whfoods.com/genpage.php?tname=foodspice&dbid=84

128. Wolfe, <u>Eating for Beauty</u>, ibid, 41-42

129. Servan-Schreiber, David <u>Anti Cancer: A New Way of Life</u>, "Anticancer Action" insert (New York: Vikin/Penguin, 2008), 9-11

130. Cimons, Marlene "Exercise Builds a Reputation Against Cancer" Los Angeles Times, 24 Dec. 2001 |article online|; available from http://articles.latimes.com/2001/dec/24/health/he-cancer24

131. Mallet, Karen "Lombardi Study: Vigorous Exercise Appears to Dramatically Cut Breast Cancer Risk in African American Women" Georgetown Lombardi Medical Center, 1 Oct. 2010 |press release online|; available from http://explore.georgetown.edu/documents/52841/?PageTemplateID=141

132. Chandler JM, Hadley EC "Exercise to Improve Physiologic and Functional Performance in Old Age" Clinics in Geriatric Medicine 12(4) (1996): 761-784 |abstract online|; available from http://europepmc.org/abstract/MED/8890115/reload=0;jsessionid=up7KZbXmtIj3iqr48yu8.10

133. WebMD "Exercise and Depression" WebMD.com, Depression Health Center, n.d. |article online|; available from http://www.webmd.com/depression/guide/exercise-depression

134. WebMD, ibid.

135. Underwood, Estelle "Exercise: More Effective Than Antidepressants?" The Huffington Post, Huffingtonpost.com, 6 Nov. 2011 |article online|; available from http://www.huffingtonpost.com/estelle-underwood/suffering-from-depression_b_1077889.html

136. Wolfe and Shazzie, <u>Naked Chocolate</u>, ibid, 15.

Questions for community discussion?

Post responses online at www.ripestcherry.com, or mail to:
Honest Abe Press, P.O. Box 618, Topanga, CA 90290
Handwritten correspondences may appear in the next
issue of "No Sweeter Than The Ripest Cherry!"

Q: Let's assume that our herbivorous bodies have adapted in the short term to tolerate meats and cooked food -- as evidenced by the potent digestive enzymes we produce. And let's also assume that this adaptation of "extra enzymes" accounts for the miracles of healing so many raw food-ists experience once their "enzyme reserve" is freed to assist with systemic rejuvenation. Is it then possible these "extra adapted enzymes" -- which afford longevity, vitality and superior health to many raw foodists -- are an advantage only cultivated through the centuries long, multi-generational consumption of animal products and cooked foods?

Q: Given that evolution is a function of natural selection acting upon personal choices and advantageous genetic traits, and humankind evolved as committed herbivores but began consuming meat as an aspect of survival; what is gained from the continued consumption of animal products in light of their evidenced connection with the proliferation of cancers, heart disease, and other ailments? Or do SOME animal products provide a nutritional advantage that warrents their inclusion?

Q: Lastly, how might we consciously direct our continued evolution with our dietary choices? Could the differences in our current dietary preferences actually be a function of evolution in action?!

Acknowledgements

This comic book was made possible by the unwaivering faith and support of my very good friend Waska Lamb, by the men and women who have devoted their lives to researching the foods we eat, and by the following brave individuals -- whose passionate pursuit to understand the mecha-nisms of the natural world has been such an inspiration to me. Your joyous motivation to share your discoveries with humankind has served the health, betterment and understanding of all. Thank you. You are my heroes. I have much love and respect for you.

Our mission is one and the same.

Anne Wigmore
Dr. Gabriel Cousens
Dr. Herbert M. Shelton
Dr. William Howard Hay
Dr. Francis M. Pottenger, III
Annie & Dr. David Jubb
Viktoras Kulvinskas
Dr. Edward Howell
Dr. J.S. Billings
Charles Darwin
David Wolfe

And the two beautiful souls who hired this then teenager to
wash dishes in their Pa'ia restaurant on Maui:

Jeremy Safron & Renée Loux

VIVA THE RAW EXPERIENCE!!!

THE END.